Emergency planning for major accidents

Control of Major Accident Hazards Regulations 1999

COMAH

HSG191

HSE BOOKS

CONTENTS

Foreword

The Control of Major Accident Hazards Regulations 1999 (COMAH) implement the Seveso II Directive, and are important for controlling major accident hazards involving dangerous substances in Great Britain. The Regulations are enforced by a 'competent authority', comprising HSE and either the Environment Agency or Scottish Environment Protection Agency. It is for this reason that this guidance is a joint publication.

The Regulations aim to prevent major accidents involving dangerous substances and to limit the consequences to people and the environment if accidents do occur. COMAH requires on-site and off-site emergency plans to deal with potential major accidents for those sites with the greatest hazards.

This book is a practical guide for those who have to prepare emergency plans, and for those who have to respond to them, including operators, local authorities, emergency services, and health authorities and health boards.

If you were previously involved in emergency planning under the Control of Industrial Major Accident Hazards Regulations 1984 (CIMAH), you will find that there are differences in the requirements. For instance, there are new requirements on consultation and on testing emergency plans. This book will help you to identify the issues you should consider during the emergency planning process.

We commend this guidance to you.

Signed:

Jenny Bacon
(Director General, HSE)

Ed Gallagher
(Chief Executive,
Environment Agency)

Alasdair C Paton
(Chief Executive,
(Scottish Environment
Protection Agency)

Introduction

Purpose

1   The purpose of this document is to provide further guidance on good practice for emergency planning, with reference to the emergency planning regulations (regulations 9-12) of the Control of Major Accident Hazards Regulations 1999 (COMAH). This guidance supplements the guidance on the COMAH Regulations[1] and the guidance on preparing safety reports under COMAH.[2] The information will be of use to all those with responsibilities for emergency planning, on site and off site, at major hazards establishments including: operators; local authorities; emergency services; and health authorities/boards.

Background

2   COMAH implements the Seveso II Directive (96/82/EC) which replaces the original Seveso Directive (82/501/EEC), implemented in Great Britain by the Control of Industrial Major Accident Hazards Regulations 1984 (CIMAH). The CIMAH Regulations are now revoked. The new Regulations aim to prevent major accidents involving dangerous substances and to limit the consequences to people and the environment of any accidents that do occur.

3   This document (HSG191) replaces the emergency planning guidance produced by the Health and Safety Executive (HSE) for the CIMAH Regulations: HSG25. This new guidance reflects the changes introduced on emergency planning in COMAH.

4   On pages 3, 16-17, 20-22 and 27, the text in white and bold italics is taken directly from the COMAH Regulations.

Competent authority

5   A key feature of COMAH is that the Regulations are enforced by a competent authority comprising HSE and the Environment Agency (EA), in England and Wales, and HSE and the Scottish Environment Protection Agency (SEPA) in Scotland. The bodies comprising the competent authority work jointly, and operators will generally receive a single response on all matters to do with COMAH.

Application

6   An establishment is subject to COMAH if it has on site any substance specified in Schedule 1 of COMAH above the qualifying quantity. There are two threshold quantities:

(a)   establishments with quantities equal to or greater than the upper threshold are known as top-tier establishments; and

(b)   establishments with lower quantities, but which are equal to or greater than the lower threshold, are known as lower-tier establishments.

7   Further details about the thresholds can be found in the guidance to Schedule 1 of COMAH. Even if threshold quantities of substances are not present at an establishment, it may still be subject to COMAH if specified dangerous substances could be produced in threshold quantities following the loss of control of an industrial chemical process - see Schedule 1 of COMAH for further details.

Top-tier duties

8   If any top-tier threshold is exceeded then additional duties are imposed by regulations 7 to 14 of COMAH, for example regulation 14 covers information which must be provided to the public including safety reports. Regulations 9 to 12 cover emergency planning requirements, including the need to test both on-site and off-site emergency plans, which is a new duty on operators and local authorities. Charging for emergency planning is covered in regulation 13, and further details can be found in the guidance on COMAH.

9   Operators must not only take all the measures necessary to comply with the Regulations but they must, when requested by the competent authority, demonstrate that they have done so (regulation 15(1)). The competent authority's programme of inspections is designed to check this. For top-tier operators this means ensuring that the plant is operated in accordance with the information and data in the safety report. For further information see the COMAH guidance on regulations 15 and 19.

10   Operators of top-tier sites are required to produce a safety report, the key requirement of which is a demonstration that they have taken all measures necessary to prevent major accidents and to limit the consequences to people and the environment of any that do occur.

Lower-tier duties

11   The emergency planning requirements of COMAH apply to top-tier establishments, but this guidance may be useful for lower-tier establishments in setting up their emergency arrangements in the major accident prevention policy (MAPP), as required by regulation 5 of COMAH.

12   If the lower-tier threshold is exceeded, operators must notify the competent authority and provide the details in Schedule 3 of COMAH. This is a new feature in COMAH; previously only top-tier operators were required

to make such a notification. Notification should be given to the local office of HSE's Chemical and Hazardous Installations Division. Details will be passed to the relevant office of EA or SEPA in accordance with the competent authority arrangements. Lower-tier operators must also take 'all measures necessary' to prevent major accidents, and they must report major accidents. These are developments of existing CIMAH duties.

13   The most important new duty on lower-tier operators is the preparation of a MAPP. This duty reflects the vital role of management systems in accident prevention. The essential elements of a safety management system which must be included in the MAPP are given in Schedule 2 of COMAH. This starts with the company policy on major accidents, and then details the organisational structure, responsibilities, procedures, etc, for implementing it.

14   For lower-tier sites, the MAPP must be reviewed and, if necessary, revised in the event of certain modifications. This is an extension of the duties to address management of change and to audit and review the MAPP document under Schedule 2. This duty is aimed at modifications which could have significant repercussions on major accident hazards and is not intended to deal with routine or trivial changes.

15   More details on MAPP can be found in the COMAH guidance to regulation 5.

16   All operators, whether top or lower-tier, must have adequate safety management systems in place. The difference between the two tiers of duty is largely the extent to which the systems have to be documented.

Further information

17   In addition to this guidance, the guidance on COMAH and guidance on preparing a COMAH safety report, duty holders and others can put further questions on COMAH to the local offices of HSE, EA or SEPA.

Legal requirements

COMAH Regulations

Top-tier sites

18   COMAH implements into British legislation the European Community Directive on the control of major accident hazards involving dangerous substances, known as the Seveso II Directive. However, COMAH does not implement the land-use planning requirements of the Directive in Article 12; these are being implemented by planning legislation.[3] COMAH requires operators of top-tier establishments to prepare and keep up to date on-site emergency plans and to supply necessary information to their local authority, who are required to prepare an off-site emergency plan. Schedule 5 of COMAH contains details of the objectives and the information that should be included in emergency plans.

Objectives of on-site and off-site emergency plans

19   Schedule 5, Part 1 of COMAH describes the objectives of emergency plans which are referred to in regulations 9(1) and 10(1). These objectives are stated as follows:

> *(1) containing and controlling incidents so as to minimise the effects, and to limit damage to persons, the environment and property;*
>
> *(2) implementing the measures necessary to protect persons and the environment from the effects of major accidents;*
>
> *Regulations*

> *(3) communicating the necessary information to the public and to the emergency services and authorities concerned in the area;*
>
> *(4) providing for the restoration and clean-up of the environment following a major accident.*
>
> *Regulations*

20   COMAH specifies when the plans for top-tier establishments should be produced and how often they should be reviewed and revised. COMAH also requires that the emergency plans are tested.

21   For top-tier establishments, two emergency plans have to be produced in writing:

(a)   **the on-site emergency plan,** which is prepared by the operator, to specify the response to the emergency of those who work on the site;

(b)   **the off-site emergency plan,** which is prepared by the local authority, to specify the co-ordinated response of agencies to an emergency on the site, which has off-site effects.

22   The two emergency plans should detail how they 'dovetail' together. The on-site emergency plan should include the arrangements that the operator has in place to assist with the emergency response off-site; the off-site emergency plan should include details of the arrangements for providing assistance to the on-site emergency response.

23   The Home Office publication *Dealing with disaster*[4] and the Scottish Office publication *Dealing with disasters together*[5] contain guidelines for local authorities, emergency services and others (see paragraph 106). These highlight the importance of a combined response from all agencies involved, ie integrated arrangements for emergency management at the planning, response and recovery phases, including planning, training and exercising.

24   For further details on organisations with roles to play in major accidents, see Appendix 3.

25   Employees and others who work on site, and the emergency services, have to be consulted about the on-site emergency plan (see paragraph 38 for the complete list of statutory consultees). For the off-site emergency plan, the emergency services and the public should be consulted (see paragraph 39 for the complete list of statutory consultees). Public consultation will normally be carried out through elected representatives or through specially established groups representing residents in the vicinity of the establishment.

Lower-tier sites

26   For lower-tier establishments, the major accident prevention policy (MAPP) required by regulation 5 of COMAH should include information on the management system and specifically the procedures for identifying foreseeable emergencies. These procedures should not ignore the reasonably foreseeable, low probability, high consequence events, such as catastrophic vessel failure. The level of planning for these emergencies should be proportional to the probability of the accident occurring. The MAPP should also detail how the operator will prepare, test and review plans to respond to such foreseeable emergencies (see Schedule 2 paragraph 4(e)).

Other legal requirements

27   COMAH is not the only legislation requiring emergency planning. There are many activities not subject to the top-tier requirements of COMAH which could present the risk of a major accident and which may require the preparation of arrangements for dealing with emergencies. The following legislation may apply to these activities, for both top-tier and lower-tier sites:

(a)   **The Health and Safety at Work etc Act 1974,** which applies to all work activities, establishes basic principles for ensuring the safety and health of people liable to be affected by work activities;

(b)   **The Management of Health and Safety at Work Regulations 1999,** which apply to all work activities, require employers and the self-employed to identify the hazards arising from their activities and make suitable arrangements to ensure that they are properly controlled. The Regulations require the establishment of procedures to be followed in the event of serious and imminent danger;

(c)   **The Nuclear Installations Act 1965,** requires nuclear installations licensed under the Act to have in place adequate arrangements for dealing with emergencies (Licence Condition 11);

(d)   **The Pipeline Safety Regulations 1996,** require emergency plans to be prepared for major accident hazard pipelines.

28   Other legislation requiring contingency or emergency planning includes: the Ionising Radiations Regulations 1985 (soon to be replaced by revised regulations on ionising radiations and new regulations on radiation emergency preparedness); the Dangerous Substances in Harbour Areas Regulations 1987; and the Genetically Modified Organisms (Contained Use) Regulations 1992.

General issues on emergency planning

Why have an emergency plan?

29   As detailed in the previous chapter, emergency planning is a legal requirement for some employers' establishments. In all cases where a major accident could occur, which could result in serious harm to people or the environment, proper planning will assist in minimising the consequences. Good planning will also optimise the use of resources.

30   The emergency plan should address the response required during every phase of the emergency, both the immediate needs and the longer term recovery. The first few hours after the accident occurs is the 'critical' phase of an accident response, when key decisions, which will greatly affect the success of any mitigation measures, must be made under considerable pressure and within a short period of time. Therefore, a detailed understanding of the likely sequence of events and appropriate countermeasures will greatly benefit anyone who may reasonably be expected to have a role to play.

31   In the event of an inquiry, following a major accident, the emergency plan will be useful to demonstrate that the parties concerned had done all that was reasonable for them to do in preparing for such an event.

32   Emergency planning is part of an overall strategy for preventing and minimising the effects of major accidents to people and the environment. There are three basic parts of this major accident strategy, proposed by the Advisory Committee on Major Hazards. This Committee was appointed by the Health and Safety Commission to consider the problems of major accident hazards and to make recommendations, following the Flixborough accident of 1974. The three parts are:

(a)   **Identification** - establishments holding more than specified quantities of dangerous substances should notify their presence to the enforcing authority;

(b)   **Prevention and control -** by applying appropriate controls based on an assessment of the hazards, risks and possible consequences, the likelihood of a major accident can be minimised; and

(c)   **Mitigation -** even with the best controls, major accidents will never be totally eliminated so the effects of any that do occur should be kept as small as possible. Emergency planning is one of the principal steps to achieving this.

33   The guidance documents *Dealing with disaster* and *Dealing with disasters together* detail the main planning stages associated with an emergency plan: assessment, prevention, preparedness, response and recovery (see paragraphs 23 and 106 for further details).

Who is responsible for emergency planning?

34   The operator and the local authority each has a duty to ensure that the appropriate plans are prepared and are adequate for the purpose, ie the operator is responsible for the on-site plan,

and the local authority has responsibility for the off-site plan. In each case, the exchange of information between the planner and other organisations with an interest, is central to the planning process and there needs to be extensive consultation with all those parties.

35   All those organisations with a reasonably foreseeable role in the overall emergency response and recovery must be involved, as appropriate, in the preparation of the emergency plans. Many of their interests will overlap and may, on occasion, conflict. Co-operation is essential, and compromise may sometimes be necessary. Senior representatives of the principal organisations which could have a role to play in an emergency should meet as a senior emergency co-ordinating group, or other similar group, to develop the plan and the testing regime, and to consult other organisations.

36   Following a major accident, the establishment of a strategic co-ordinating group (SCG) is recommended good practice in the guidance documents *Dealing with disaster* and *Dealing with disasters together*. Such a group would have a remit to ensure that all agencies involved in the disaster response are adequately prepared, and that the multi-agency approach is properly co-ordinated. The SCG should consist of the chief officers of the emergency services, local authority chief executives and senior NHS personnel.

37   The functions of the principal organisations, who could have roles in the on-site or off-site emergency planning process for major accident hazards, are outlined in Appendix 3.

Who is consulted on emergency planning?

38   For on-site emergency plans, the statutory consultees under COMAH, in addition to those employed on the establishment, are:

(a)   the fire service;

(b)   the police service;

(c)   the ambulance service;

(d)   if appropriate, the Coastguard Agency;

(e)   the health authority (as defined in COMAH to include health boards in Scotland);

(f)   the Environment Agency (EA) or Scottish Environment Protection Agency (SEPA); and

(g)   the local authority, if there is the requirement for an off-site emergency plan.

39   For off-site emergency plans, the statutory consultees under COMAH, in addition to the operator, are:

(a)   the competent authority - HSE, and EA or SEPA (see the Introduction for further details);

(b)   the fire service;

(c)   the police service;

(d)   the ambulance service;

(e)   if appropriate, the Coastguard Agency;

(f)   the health authority where the site is, plus any other relevant health authorities nearby (eg if near a boundary); and

(g)   members of the public the local authority considers appropriate, eg consultation with elected councillors at county, borough or parish level (or equivalents), or with specially established groups representing residents in the vicinity of the site.

40   COMAH requires those employed on the establishment to be consulted on the contents of the on-site emergency plan. This may be direct, using discussion groups or working groups, or may be via suitably elected employee representatives.

41   COMAH also requires consultation with the emergency services identified as having a role to play in the on-site emergency response, and with the appropriate Agency (EA or SEPA). The emergency services roles should be discussed and agreed before inclusion in the on-site emergency arrangements. This will also enable dovetailing with the emergency services response plans.

42   Where an establishment is required to have an off-site emergency plan, COMAH makes the local authority a statutory consultee for the on-site emergency plan. This is to ensure a high degree of dovetailing between the on-site and off-site plans.

43   The local authority with responsibility for the development of an off-site emergency plan under COMAH should consult with the operator, the competent authority (HSE and EA or SEPA), the emergency services, the health authorities in the vicinity of the establishment, and such members of the public that it considers appropriate.

44   The health authorities have a responsibility for public health, and they should have in place arrangements for the control of environmental hazards which includes chemical releases. They should ensure that suitable arrangements are in place at the hospital accident and emergency units that would be expected to receive casualties from major accidents addressed by the emergency plans.

45   The consultation with the public that the local authority considers appropriate may be via elected representatives at district, county, unitary authority, community or parish/town level, and in Scotland also at community council or area forum level. It may also take place via appropriately constituted local liaison groups for the population in the immediate vicinity of a major hazard establishment. Many establishments already have liaison groups of this nature to provide links between the operators and the local community. These groups can act as suitable routes for the resolution of grievances between establishments and those who live in the vicinity. But they can also enable the operators to keep their neighbours fully informed of their activities.

46   Where groups of this nature exist, they are a suitable forum for consultation on the contents of the off-site emergency plan by the local authority. A sub-committee of the liaison group may be established to act as a focus for detailed discussions on the contents of the off-site emergency plan. This would provide a channel of communication between the operator, local authority, emergency services and other organisations with a role to play in the event of an emergency, as well as with representatives of those living in the vicinity of the establishment.

47   It may also be necessary to consult with other organisations in addition to those specifically identified by the Regulations. These are organisations who might become involved in the response to a major accident, and their roles would need to be included in the off-site emergency plan. Such organisations may include: the Ministry of Agriculture, Fisheries and Food; the Welsh Office, Agriculture Department; the Scottish Office Agriculture, Environment and Fisheries Department, and water companies/authorities.

How are the emergency plans produced?

48   The mechanism for producing emergency plans needs to be structured to ensure that when activated, the plan produces an adequate response to a major accident.

49   COMAH sets out the principal objectives of emergency plans, which are reproduced in paragraph 19.

50   Key components of the emergency planning process are:

(a)   Identification of the significant sources, types, scales and consequences of potential major accidents, including malicious acts;

(b)   establishment of the objectives of the response, both technical and organisational;

(c)   identification of the components (procedures, roles and resources - hardware and software) required to achieve the response;

(d)   identification of the organisations and key post holders involved;

(e)   identification of the expertise, arrangements and capabilities of the organisations and individuals which are relevant to the procedures and the roles needed, and the adequacy of the resources identified for responding to the identified major accident scenarios;

(f) determination of how all the responses will be co-ordinated including any 'sub-plans' (see paragraph 55), eg any standing arrangements within the emergency services;

(g) allocation of responsibilities for the response and associated components;

(h) identification of situations where the routine procedures and resources are not appropriate or sufficient, and what to do instead. This includes how to recognise when the change from routine is necessary and how to implement change; and

(i) identification of the means to ensure the plans will be put into effect as intended - this is a duty under COMAH.

51   The HSE publication *Preparing safety reports* contains further information on producing a COMAH safety report.

52   Emergency plans should be based on the specific needs of each particular establishment, the foreseeable emergencies which may arise, and the arrangements for dealing with those emergencies. Emergency plans should address the full range of possible major accidents foreseen for the establishment concerned, but the degree of planning should be proportional to the probability of the accident occurring. For on-site emergency plans, the major accident hazards identified in the safety report should form the basis of the emergency planning for COMAH establishments. Reasonably foreseeable, low probability, high consequence events, such as catastrophic vessel failure, should be considered. However, if the probability of these occurring is very low then the amount of detail need not be great.

53   The on-site emergency plan should include details of normal and special control arrangements for dealing with the major accident scenarios that have been foreseen. The arrangements will vary according to circumstances, and they should take account of the size and complexity of the establishment, the nature of the processes and the materials handled, the number of people employed, the availability of resources and the location of the establishment. Appendix 1 provides further information on examples of hazardous events.

54   The on-site emergency plan should be an aspect of the overall safety management system. The plan should comprise suitable and co-ordinated arrangements that should ensure that all the necessary people, resources and information are available and brought into action, to deal in an appropriate manner with the whole range of reasonably foreseeable emergencies.

55   The various parts of the overall on-site or off-site emergency plans may be regarded as sub-plans. These need to be effectively co-ordinated during the planning process.

56   Some components of the emergency plan are primarily about the response, for example:

(a) when and how to call the emergency services;

(b) who will take charge and what they will be responsible for;

(c) relevant procedures for the response;

(d) special procedures for dealing with particular circumstances;

(e) availability of resources including the requirement of any specialist equipment;

(f) where and how to get information;

(g) how the emergency responders can be easily identified including how they can identify each other; and

(h) where the emergency responders can rendezvous and how they will communicate.

57   Other components are primarily about making the plan work, for example:

(a) training for emergency planners;

(b) training for people with roles to play in connection with the plan;

(c) how plan components will be tested;

(d) how plan components will be updated;

(e) how plan components will be reviewed and revised to take account of changes or lessons learned.

58   Emergency plans must be documented in writing. The documentation should be a record of agreements and procedures which cover all the appropriate people and organisations, all the necessary resources, and the full range of major accident situations anticipated.

59   Plans should be as concise as possible but not at the expense of essential detail.

60   A large part of the emergency plan preparation is about the exchange of information and ideas between people and organisations. Serious consideration should be given to the most effective way of carrying this out for the circumstances of a particular emergency plan. There are numerous possible approaches. In addition to the obvious communication methods, via telephone, letter or fax, there are:

(a)   steering groups;

(b)   emergency planning working groups;

(c)   meetings of a selection of the organisations involved;

(d)   discussion or focus groups; and

(e)   briefing or review meetings.

61   Specific advance consideration must also be given to forming links between those delegated to handle media relations on behalf of the various response agencies. This should ensure that any statements released to the media and public on issues, including public health, are jointly agreed and approved by all parties. This also includes information provided through public helplines.

When should emergency plans be prepared?

62   Under COMAH, operators of existing top-tier CIMAH sites which *became top-tier establishments on 1 April 1999 have until 3 February 2001* to prepare a COMAH on-site emergency plan and to supply the appropriate information to the local authority.

63   Operators of other existing establishments which *became top-tier establishments on 1 April 1999* (ie those which were lower-tier CIMAH sites or did not fall under the CIMAH Regulations) have until *3 February 2002* to prepare a COMAH on-site emergency plan and to supply the appropriate information to the local authority.

64   For operators of establishments which *become top-tier COMAH after 1 April 1999*, the on-site emergency plan should be prepared *prior to starting operation*. The operator should also, before the start of operation, inform the local authority and give them information to allow the authority to prepare the off-site emergency plan. The local authority should also be consulted on the aspects of the on-site emergency plan which are significant for the off-site plan.

65   The local authority has six months from:

(a)   being notified by the competent authority that a plan is needed;

(b)   the date by which the operator must prepare the on-site plan; or

(c)   receipt of the information needed to prepare the plan;

whichever is the latest, to prepare an off-site emergency plan as required by COMAH. The competent authority may extend this period to a maximum of nine months under specific circumstances. The competent authority would expect to see evidence that work is being undertaken to produce the off-site emergency plan as soon as possible. Top-tier CIMAH sites will already have on-site and off-site emergency plans in place.

66   It is recommended good practice that initial interim arrangements are put in to place, until the COMAH off-site emergency plan is finalised. These can be based on the generic emergency planning arrangements, utilising any existing CIMAH or other emergency plans, and the information supplied by the operator. The arrangements should be developed in consultation with the emergency services to give direction for coping with any incidents that have off-site consequences. This could include the preparation of interim action sheets for the operator, local authority, emergency services, health authorities/boards and other response agencies.

67   In the case of a new major hazard establishment, with the potential to have accidents with off-site consequences, the operator would be expected to enter into discussions with the local authority emergency planning team about the hazards and risks that the new establishment may present. This would allow early work to start on the preparation of the off-site emergency plan. In practice, there are considerable benefits to be gained from developing the on-site and off-site emergency plans in parallel. In this way, the common information needs of the staff producing the on-site plan and the local authority emergency planners can be addressed. In addition, the dovetailing of the two plans can be maximised to reduce inefficiencies in planning and execution.

68   Operators of lower-tier COMAH establishments should include emergency planning within their major accident prevention policy (MAPP). This duty reflects the vital role of management systems in accident prevention.

Use of emergency plans

69   Emergency plans are 'living' documents. They should be kept up to date and put into effect without delay whenever needed. All those with agreed roles and responsibilities within the plans should carry them out when, where and how they have been agreed.

70   The principles outlined in the plan should be followed during training, testing and in the event of a genuine major accident. It is helpful to include checklists in the plan as a guide to informed decision making and as a series of reminders for individuals.

71   The plan should contain all the information that those responding to an emergency may reasonably expect. The procedures that it contains for individual job holders should be simple and straightforward, should not be contradictory, and should enable maximum flexibility of response, relative to the size of the establishment.

72   The plan should include arrangements for:

(a)   bringing together the people who would have to deal with an accident, for assessing the possible consequences and implementing co-ordinated response procedures;

(b)   alerting contacts both in and out of working hours; and

(c)   ensuring provision of information to the public who might be affected by an accident.

73   The plan should also include any establishment specific data that might be needed for making operational decisions in response to an accident.

Information required for emergency plans

74   In developing the safety report required by COMAH, the operators of top-tier establishments need to describe the equipment installed in the plant to limit the consequences of major accidents, the organisation of alert and intervention, the extent of mobilisable resources and how they will be used to develop the on-site emergency plan. Further guidance is available in the HSE publication *Preparing safety reports*.

75   Local authority emergency planners require the following key pieces of information from the operator's safety report:

(a)   What hazards are present, ie:

   (i)   what are the possible sources of harm?

   (ii)   what are the dangerous substances, the quantities, their location, their properties and their potential effects on people and the environment?

   (iii)   if feasible, what are the reactions of chemicals released and their behaviour in fires, or are there sources of specialist assistance and references? Operators should also consider substances which may be generated during the loss of control of an industrial chemical process.

(b)   What are the sources of major accidents, ie what events could give rise to a release of dangerous substances?

(c)   What are the possible consequences of a release of dangerous substances to people and to the environment?

(d) Over what distances can these hazards create harmful effects, ie how far from the source will these substances be dangerous to people and to the environment; what level of harm will they pose and under what circumstances? The harm may be immediate or delayed.

(e) What are the probabilities of these consequences being realised, ie how likely and how potentially serious are the events? A risk assessment will be included in the safety report.

76   In addition, the emergency planners require outline information on:

(a) how the hazards are already controlled;

(b) what additional measures would be needed if the normal controls fail or prove to be inadequate;

(c) any special characteristics which may require a response different from the routine;

(d) what systems and resources are already in place for dealing with different circumstances, and how far they go towards satisfying the response needed; and

(e) what further capabilities are available from other organisations potentially involved in the response.

77   The fire service require specific information, under section (1) of the Fire Services Act 1947, for the development of their arrangements for dealing with a major hazard accident. Operators should co-operate as much as possible with the fire service in the collection of this information (see Appendix 2 for further details).

On-site emergency plans

Scope

78 The COMAH on-site emergency plan encompasses the operator's complete response to a major accident involving dangerous substances on the establishment. The on-site plan should concentrate on those events identified as being most likely to occur. The level of planning should be proportional to the probability of the accident occurring. The plan should have the flexibility to allow it to be extended and increased to deal with extremely unlikely consequences which may arise through combinations of accidental circumstances and weather conditions.

79 The on site plan should detail how the operator prepares people on the establishment for an emergency (people includes all those who may be on site at any time such as operatives, supervisors, managerial staff, non-production staff, contract workers and visitors), and how to control, contain and mitigate the effects of any emergency. The on-site plan should also detail how assistance from other organisations off site will be summoned, and how those who work on the establishment will assist any external organisations, including assisting with off-site mitigatory action.

80 If COMAH and other legislation requiring emergency plans (for example, the Nuclear Installations Act 1965) apply to the same site, then the operator may prepare a single emergency plan to cover all the requirements.

Key personnel

81 In order to make the best use of available resources in the event of an emergency, and to avoid confusion, the on-site emergency plan should identify nominated key personnel (by name or by job title). It is recommended that the names and telephone numbers of authorised personnel are included in the annexes of the emergency plan, as this will facilitate updating changes.

82 COMAH requires the on-site emergency plan to include the names or positions of people authorised to set the emergency procedures in motion, and of the person in charge of co-ordinating the on-site mitigatory response. These two principal functions are usually, in the event of an emergency, carried out by the 'site incident controllor' and the 'site main controller' (see paragraphs 83 to 86 for a fuller explanation of the roles). It is possible that on smaller sites that the site incident controller and the site main controller roles can be assigned to the same person.

Site incident controller

83 The site incident controller is responsible for taking control at the scene of the incident. The person carrying out this role should have a thorough knowledge of the overall situation in the vicinity of the incident. This is particularly important in the case where establishment operations are closely interlinked. A suitable job function to fill this role is the establishment manager, shift manager or shift supervisor at the time the incident occurred. Round-the-clock

cover to fulfil this role is essential. On establishments with a small number of staff, or which are not attended around the clock, appropriate management arrangements should be in place to carry out the necessary functions in an emergency.

Responsibilities

84 The responsibilities of the site incident controller should include the following:

(a) As soon as the site incident controller has been made aware of an incident, they should assess it to determine if it is, or may develop into, a major accident. If so, the on-site emergency plan should be activated and, if appropriate, the off-site emergency plan as well.

(b) The site incident controller should assume the responsibilities of the site main controller until the latter is in place. In particular, responsibility should be taken for:

   (i) ensuring that the emergency services are alerted;

   (ii) ensuring that appropriate establishment alarms are sounded and the public has been informed;

   (iii) directing the shutting down and evacuation of other plant areas that are likely to be affected; and

   (iv) ensuring that appropriate key personnel are summoned.

(c) The main function of the site incident controller is to direct all operations in the event of a major accident at the scene. The main responsibilities are:

   (i) control of rescue and fire-fighting operations, until the arrival of the emergency services, when control will normally be passed over to a senior fire officer;

   (ii) working with the fire service in the search for casualties; and

   (iii) evacuation of non-essential workers to assembly areas.

(d) The site incident controller should also take responsibility for:

   (i) setting up a communication point with appropriate communication equipment, for contact with the 'emergency control centre(s)' (ECC);

   (ii) giving advice and information, as requested, to the emergency services at the scene (primarily the fire service); and

   (iii) briefing the site main controller and keeping the on-site ECC informed of all significant developments.

Site main controller

85 The site main controller has the overall responsibility for directing operations from the on-site ECC. A suitable job function to fill this role is the senior establishment manager, establishment manager or director who has an overall knowledge of the site.

Responsibilities

86 The responsibilities of the site main controller should include the following:

(a) The site main controller should go to the on-site ECC and, at that point, take over responsibility for overall control from the site incident controller.

(b) If a major emergency exists, the site main controller should confirm that the emergency services have been summoned and, if appropriate, that the off-site emergency plan has been initiated.

(c) Depending upon circumstances, the site main controller should:

   (i) ensure that the key personnel are mobilised;

   (ii) ensure that direct operational control is available for those parts of the establishment outside the areas directly affected;

(iii) review and assess developments, as appropriate, to help predict the most likely development of the incident;

(iv) direct the shutting down of plants and evacuation of buildings, as appropriate, in consultation with the site incident controller and key personnel;

(v) ensure that casualties are receiving adequate attention and, if appropriate, arrange for additional assistance. They should also ensure, in liaison with the police, that relatives are kept informed of missing and injured people;

(vi) establish contacts, as appropriate, with agencies able to give prior information on impending changes in weather conditions;

(vii) liaise with appropriate external agencies to provide advice on possible effects on areas outside the establishment. Such agencies would include senior officers of fire, ambulance and police services, the relevant Agency (EA or SEPA), HSE and the health authority;

(viii) ensure that all personnel are accounted for;

(ix) control traffic movement within the establishment;

(x) arrange for an ongoing record to be kept of the emergency and the responses undertaken to mitigate its effects, to provide evidence of the decisions made, the mitigatory action taken, and to ensure that lessons are learned from the response to the emergency;

(xi) provide for the welfare needs of establishment personnel, for example the provision of food and drinks, relief and the means to keep relatives informed;

(xii) establish links with news media and issue information and statements, as appropriate, in liaison with the emergency services;

(xiii) ensure that full consideration is given to the preservation of evidence; and

(xiv) control the rehabilitation of affected areas after the emergency.

On-site emergency control centre (ECC)

87　The principal facility that should be considered in the on-site emergency plan is the on-site ECC, the place from which operations to manage the response to the emergency are directed and co-ordinated. This will normally be the location occupied by the site main controller, other key personnel as appropriate, and by the senior officers of the emergency services in attendance for tactical and operational command and control.

88　The on-site ECC should have good communication links with the site incident controller and all other installations on the establishment, as well as communication with appropriate points off site, which may be via the on-site emergency services. These links should include emergency services' headquarters, hospitals and the health authority, company headquarters, regulatory authorities and the media (to assist early distribution of public health and safety advice to minimise delay). However, once the off-site ECC is set up, the media contact and enquiries will be via the off-site ECC media liaison representative. The on-site media contact is an interim measure.

89　The on-site ECC requires facilities to record the development of the incident to assist in its management and in decision making on the appropriate method of control. Records will also need to be kept for any subsequent inquiry.

90　On-site ECCs generally have to contain the following:

(a) Equipment for adequate external off-site communications. This includes mechanisms for communications - in and out - dedicated to emergency response personnel (eg telephones and fax machines), which ensure they do not get overwhelmed with communications from concerned neighbours and relatives, and the media. Communication arrangements need to be established for the emergency services, to link them to their central control facilities.

(b) Equipment for adequate internal (on-site) communications. This may be via an internal telephone system, radio links or some other means.

(c) Site plans and maps to show clearly the current on-site location of:

(i) the areas where hazardous materials are transported, stored and processed, including lorry parks, rail, tanks, reactors, critical pipework, storage drums and cylinders;

(ii) any radioactive material in use or storage;

(iii) safety equipment;

(iv) firewater supplies, the routing of firewater mains and the location of any additional sources of water;

(v) drains and outfalls to watercourses;

(vi) any other fire-fighting materials, eg specifying the foam concentrate type and percentage;

(vii) access points to the establishment and the on-site road system. This should be annotated to indicate which access points and routes may become unusable as the incident develops;

(viii) key transport facilities for emergency services, loading and unloading, and evacuation of employees;

(ix) assembly points and casualty treatment centres;

(x) the establishment relative to the surrounding community, identifying any vulnerable populations (for example hospitals, nurseries and schools) or environmental features.

(d) Site plans which can be marked up to show the development of the incident and the deployment of emergency response resources, areas evacuated and other related information.

(e) Facilities to ensure that a record is kept of all messages sent and received.

(f) Access to data on all those present on the site at the time of the incident.

(g) Appropriate contact numbers for all personnel with a role to play in the response to the incident.

91 Careful consideration should be given to the location of the on-site ECC, taking into account the likely location(s) of the sources of major accidents on the site. The on-site ECC should be designed to remain operational in all but the most severe emergency. However for large establishments, or where a toxic release is a reasonably foreseeable accident scenario, it may be appropriate to set up two control centres to ensure that under most circumstances, eg accounting for different wind directions, one is available should the other be disabled.

Contents of an on-site emergency plan

92 The following text expands on the requirements in Schedule 5, Part 2 of COMAH, 'Information to be included in on-site emergency plan'.

> *(1) Names or positions of persons authorised to set emergency procedures in motion and the person in charge of and co-ordinating the on-site mitigatory action.*
>
> *Regulations*

93 The plan should include the establishment command structure for managing the on-site response in accordance with the planned scheme, including management of the eventual clean-up and restoration. There will be times when senior managers are not available and appropriate arrangements should be included for these circumstances. It is recommended that the names and telephone numbers of authorised personnel are included in the annexes of emergency plans; this will facilitate updating changes.

(2) *Name or position of the person with responsibility for liaising with the local authority responsible for preparing the off-site emergency plan.*
Regulations

94   This is normally the person with responsibility for preparing the on-site emergency plan. It is recommended that the names and telephone numbers of authorised personnel are included in the annexes of emergency plans; this will facilitate updating changes.

(3) *For foreseeable conditions or events which could be significant in bringing about a major accident, a description of the action which should be taken to control the conditions or events and to limit their consequences, including a description of the safety equipment and the resources available.*
Regulations

95   This is the principal component of the on-site emergency plan and should include:

(a)   the types of foreseeable accidents to people or the environment;

(b)   the intended strategy for dealing with these accidents;

(c)   details of the personnel who have roles to play in the emergency response, and their responsibilities;

(d)   details of the availability and function of special emergency equipment including fire-fighting materials, and damage control and repair items; and

(e)   details of the availability and function of other resources.

(4) *Arrangements for limiting the risks to persons on site including how warnings are to be given and the actions persons are expected to take on receipt of a warning.*
Regulations

96   This should include the systems, equipment and facilities for early detection of a developing major accident, and the responsibilities for initiating the suitable responses by on-site personnel (to evacuate, shelter, use personal protective equipment, etc).

(5) *Arrangements for providing early warnings of the incident to the local authority responsible for setting the off-site emergency plan in motion, the type of information which should be contained in an initial warning and the arrangements for the provision of more detailed information as it becomes available.*
Regulations

97   This should include:

(a)   the arrangements for alerting the off-site emergency services and when this should be done (see paragraphs 196-199 for further details); and

(b)   the type of information that they will require, before and during their response, in what form, to whom and by whom.

(6) *Arrangements for training staff in the duties they will be expected to perform, and where necessary co-ordinating this with the emergency services.*
Regulations

98   This should include the arrangements for training and instructing the on-site personnel (staff, contractors, visitors, etc) and the arrangements for liaising with the off-site emergency services.

(7) *Arrangements for providing assistance with off-site mitigatory action.*
Regulations

99   This should include, for example, details of:

(a)   any special equipment, expertise or facilities which the off-site emergency services can use; and

(b)   the role of the establishment's personnel in briefing the media including the use of media briefing facilities.

Checklist for on-site emergency plans

100   The following questions may be useful in assessing the adequacy of an on-site emergency plan:

(a)   Does the plan cover the range of incidents that can be realistically anticipated?

The incidents considered should range from small events (that can be dealt with by those who work on site without any outside help) to major accidents - these need to be discussed and agreed with the emergency services and local authority. Operators of top-tier establishments should be able to justify, from the information in the safety report, the scope of the emergency plan, including:

(i)   the events considered, and why they were included or excluded;

(ii)   the typical defects and failures leading to these events;

(iii)   the timescales involved;

(iv)   the likelihood of events, so far as can reasonably be assessed; and

(v)   the options for minimising events through mitigatory action.

(b)   Have the consequences of the various incidents considered been adequately addressed?

For example, each incident should be assessed in terms of the quantity of hazardous materials that could be released as a result of an accident (including smoke effluent from fires), the rate of release, the effect of explosions, the effect of thermal radiation from fires and the effect of hazardous materials that could be released.

(c)   Are there sufficient resources in terms of personnel and equipment on the establishment, available at all times, to carry out the emergency plan for the various incidents in conjunction with the emergency services?

For example, is there sufficient water for cooling, and if this water is applied by hoses, are there sufficient trained people to operate them?

(d)   Have the timescales been assessed adequately?

(i)   While developing the emergency plan, consideration should be given to the time that will elapse between the start of an emergency and the arrival of the emergency services, and the additional time that emergency services need to deploy resources. Those who work on the establishment will have to be able to deal with the developing emergency until the off-site agencies can provide appropriate support or relief.

(ii)   Some toxic releases can develop very quickly, eg the dropping of a drum of toxic material can see the whole contents released through a sheared valve within ten minutes. If this release scenario is identified in the safety report then the subsequent remedial action should be appropriately rapid.

(e)   Is there a logical sequence of actions for the key personnel that are identified and given a role in the emergency plan?

(f)   Has suitable consultation taken place with those who work on the establishment?

(g)   Are arrangements in place to cover around the clock?

For example, is account taken of silent hours, holidays and sickness, shift handovers, and plant shutdowns?

(h)   Has there been an adequate and demonstrable level of consultation with the local authority emergency planning officers with responsibility for the development of the off-site emergency plan, and with the emergency services, to ensure adequate dovetailing between the two plans?

(i)   Has a senior emergency co-ordinating group (see paragraph 35), or other similar group been established?

(ii)   Are the arrangements in the on-site emergency plan for initiating the off-site emergency plan clear, and are they adequate?

Off-site emergency plans

Scope

101   The off-site emergency plan should be based around the major accident hazards (identified by the operator in the safety report) which could affect people and the environment outside the boundary of the establishment, or which will require the attendance of emergency services from outside the establishment if an emergency arises.

102   The plan should concentrate on those events identified as being most likely to occur. The level of planning should be proportional to the probability of the accident occurring. The plan should have the flexibility to allow it to be extended and increased to deal with extremely unlikely consequences which may arise through combinations of accidental circumstances and weather conditions.

Responsibilities

103   The competent authority will inform a local authority of the duty to produce an off-site emergency plan for a COMAH establishment within its area. The operator is required to provide the local authority with the necessary information about the nature, extent and likely effects of reasonably foreseeable major accidents. The information should be sufficiently detailed to help prepare the off-site emergency plan. The local authority can request any additional information that it may reasonably require for the preparation of the off-site emergency plan. The operator should keep a record of the information supplied to the local authority, the source of the information and how it will be reviewed, revised and updated. The local authority may use consultants or other appropriate staff when preparing the off-site emergency plan.

104   The emergency services have duties to deal with accidents and emergencies of all sorts. Therefore, the COMAH off-site emergency plan is principally a tool to co-ordinate the existing emergency services' plans, as far as possible, in their preparation for dealing with the specific hazards and risks associated with accidents on major hazard establishments. This includes identifying key personnel from a range of organisations, and defining their duties in the event of an accident. It is then possible to ensure that those identified are adequately trained to carry out these roles.

105   Local authority emergency planning staff will produce plans in liaison with the COMAH establishment staff, the competent authority, the emergency services, the health authority and appropriate members of the public. Most COMAH establishments will have been CIMAH establishments, or establishments covered by the Planning (Hazardous Substances) Act 1990[3] or the Planning (Hazardous Substances) (Scotland) Act 1997, and will therefore already be known to the planning departments of local authorities. Information received by local authorities, when requests are made for the storage or use of hazardous substances, should be automatically copied to the appropriate emergency planning department and to other appropriate agencies, eg health authorities, to allow early consideration of the implications for emergency plans of new establishments.

106 Local authorities manage a civil protection or emergency planning department. Emergency planning officers provide the focus within the community for carrying out local authority civil protection responsibilities in close co-operation with the emergency services, local authority departments, and industrial and commercial organisations, and in accordance with the current Home Office and Scottish Office emergency planning guidelines (*Dealing with disaster* in England and Wales and *Dealing with disasters together* in Scotland). These guidelines provide details of the roles and functions of emergency services and other agencies in the event of a 'disaster', which includes accidents relating to major hazards (see also paragraph 23 and Appendix 3).

107 *Dealing with disaster* states that: 'The underlying aim of integrating the arrangements for emergency management is that flexible plans will be developed which should enable any organisation to deal effectively with a major or minor emergency', which should result in the overall integration of the arrangements for emergency management. Such plans are general in nature, but they provide a framework within which COMAH off-site emergency plans can be incorporated. Therefore, existing general organisational arrangements with the emergency services, voluntary organisations and others can be used.

108 The particular arrangements for each COMAH establishment should be a self-contained document, possibly an appendix to a general plan covering several establishments. Emergency plans for establishments identified as having the potential for a domino effect (domino sites) should take this into account, and the operators involved should exchange any information necessary to allow this. Domino sites are sites where the likelihood or consequences of a major accident may be increased because of the location and close proximity of other COMAH establishments and the dangerous substances present there. These sites need special consideration in terms of emergency planning, and the testing of the off-site response.

109 It will be necessary, under some circumstances, for local authorities to liaise closely on the issue of off-site emergency planning for COMAH establishments that are very close to or which straddle the authorities' common boundary.

Contents of an off-site emergency plan

110 The following paragraphs expand on the requirements in Schedule 5, Part 3 of COMAH, 'Information to be included in an off-site emergency plan'.

> *(1) Names or positions of persons authorised to set emergency procedures in motion and of persons authorised to take charge of and co-ordinate the off-site action.*
>
> *Regulations*

111 This should include the organisation of the management for the off-site response in the event of an emergency, and include the arrangements for managing the clean-up and restoration phase of the response. The responding organisations should strive to work together as a team to maximise the effectiveness of the response to an emergency, and the response should be co-ordinated and have common basic objectives.

> *(2) Arrangements for receiving early warning of incidents, and alert and call-out procedures.*
>
> *Regulations*

112 This is primarily concerned with bringing the off-site emergency response into action. The off-site emergency plan should include details of:

(a) how a warning of a developing or actual major accident will be received by the off-site emergency services; and

(b) how the warning will be cascaded, as necessary, to the other off-site agencies involved, or liable to be involved, in the response to an emergency.

> *(3) Arrangements for co-ordinating resources necessary to implement the off-site emergency plan.*
>
> *Regulations*

113 Information should be included in the plan on how the resources identified in the response arrangements will be mobilised, and how their actions will be co-ordinated; this information

should complement and support the information required in the previous paragraphs. The information should include:

(a) which organisations have a role to play in the off-site emergency response, their roles and responsibilities;

(b) how each organisation will be alerted and will go about putting their response into action;

(c) how the emergency response personnel from the establishment and the emergency services will recognise each other at the scene;

(d) how the responding organisations and establishment personnel will communicate to obtain and transmit information needed for decision making, in accordance with their agreed roles and responsibilities;

(e) where the emergency services, the operator of the establishment and other relevant agencies will rendezvous off site, if necessary; and

(f) how they will gain access to the establishment, to any special equipment or to any other resources which may be required in the response.

(4) Arrangements for providing assistance with on-site mitigatory action. *Regulations*

114 This may, under many circumstances, mean the off-site fire service coming on to the establishment and taking over full responsibility for dealing with the response to the emergency. The following details should be included:

(a) the types of accidents that may occur to people and the environment;

(b) arrangements for briefing those arriving at the establishment on the developing emergency;

(c) the proposed emergency response strategy for dealing with the identified accident types on the establishment;

(d) the responding personnel and their responsibilities;

(e) details of the availability and applicability of special equipment including fire-fighting materials, damage control and repair items; and

(f) details of the availability and applicability of other resources which may have a role to play.

(5) Arrangements for off-site mitigatory action. *Regulations*

115 This is about dealing with accidents which have off-site consequences, for example:

(a) mitigating the off-site effects of the accident;

(b) sheltering or evacuating members of the public;

(c) controlling traffic, eg maintaining essential emergency service routes; and

(d) preventing people entering the affected area.

(6) Arrangements for providing the public with specific information relating to the accident and the behaviour which it should adopt. *Regulations*

116 The off-site emergency plan should include information on: how the public in the vicinity of the establishment will be alerted in the event of an accident; how they will be told what they should do; and how they will be told that the danger is passed and they may return to their normal activities. This will refer to the prior information that will have been supplied to those in the vicinity of the establishment as required by regulation 14 of COMAH. The public may be warned by siren, telephone, loud hailer or some other system; this is for local agreement and recording in the emergency plan. The prior information should tell the public in the vicinity of the establishment about the warning mechanism, for example the meanings of different sirens and alarms. It should be noted

that prior warning is not always possible. Regulation 14 of COMAH and its associated guidance provide further details on warning and informing arrangements.

117   The plan will also, under most circumstances, include how the media will be used to transmit information (by radio or television) for immediate dissemination (see paragraph 218). It is also important to consider within the plan how to deal with the wider media response to an emergency. The aim should be to ensure that concerns are not raised unnecessarily and that the media, and hence the public, can understand the emergency fully. This includes the consequences and potential consequences, and the response to the emergency by the operator, the emergency services and other organisations.

> **(7)   Arrangements for the provision of information to the emergency services of other Member States in the event of a major accident with possible transboundary consequences.**
>
> *Regulations*

118   This should only be required where the assessment of possible major hazard consequences shows a reasonable likelihood that there could be harmful consequences across national borders with other European Community Member States. This is unlikely to apply in Great Britain. If such a likelihood is identified, the situation should be discussed with the competent authority.

Personnel

119   The response to a major accident on site would be managed through tactical and operational levels of command and control. This should be via an on-site group consisting of those representatives of the responding organisations with the executive power to direct the resources of their organisation and who are able, if required, to call for additional resources.

Off-site emergency control centre (ECC)

120   At a strategic level, the strategic co-ordinating group (see paragraph 36) or other similar senior emergency co-ordinating group would normally convene at an off-site ECC, located at a safe distance from the accident location. The group would consist of the senior officers representing the police, fire service, ambulance service, local authority, health authority, EA or SEPA, the operator and, if appropriate, the Coastguard Agency. There may also be representatives from: the utility organisations; Ministry of Agriculture, Fisheries and Food for England; Welsh Office Agriculture Department for Wales or Scottish Office Agriculture, Environment and Fisheries Department for Scotland; and other agencies. The senior police officer will normally take the chair in the initial stages, but the group should strive to work together as a team. At a later stage it is likely that the group would be chaired by a senior local authority officer.

121   The strategic co-ordinating group or other similar senior emergency co-ordinating group at the off-site ECC should, once adequately established, take over the management of the off-site aspects of the emergency response from the on-site ECC, including the media liaison role. This will enable those on site to concentrate on the tactical and operational matters to bring the incident under control.

Derogation

122   If an operator or local authority considers that an establishment should be exempted from the requirement to produce an off-site emergency plan, they should produce and submit evidence to the competent authority. This will be based on the operator's application for derogation (dispensation) under regulation 7(12) to limit the information that is included in the safety report. The application needs to demonstrate that certain substances present on the establishment are in such a state that they cannot give rise to a major accident hazard. The application must be a specific application for one or more substances at a specified establishment, and the competent authority may grant a specific dispensation, subject to review if circumstances change.

Public health aspects of major accidents

Introduction

123 The aim of COMAH is to prevent major accidents involving dangerous substances and limit the consequences to people and the environment. To ensure that effective prevention strategies are developed and that suitable preparedness and response procedures are introduced to manage the public health aspects of major accidents, operators and local authorities should recognise the roles of health authorities/boards, acute hospital trusts, ambulance trusts and other relevant parts of the National Health Service (NHS).

124 This recognition of the roles played by the various health bodies enables:

(a) operators and local authorities to benefit from the expertise and experience of the NHS in developing, testing and revising the health-related components of their respective on-site and off-site emergency plans;

(b) the on-site and off-site emergency plans to dovetail with the plans prepared by the NHS, in accordance with the recently issued guidance *Planning for major incidents: the NHS guidance*[6] and *A manual of guidance responding to emergencies - guidance for the NHS in Scotland;*[7] and

(c) operators and local authorities to develop close working relationships with, and a detailed understanding of the respective roles and responsibilities of, the various component parts of the NHS. This includes the immediate information needs of NHS personnel involved in the management of any major accident.

Background

125 From a public health perspective, major accidents involving dangerous substances present special features which operators and local authorities should take into account in developing, testing and revising the respective emergency plans:

(a) for many chemicals, little or no information is available at present regarding their effects on human health;

(b) the source chemicals in an accident may be altered by fire, air, water, reaction with each other and by human metabolism. The possibilities are therefore infinite;

(c) casualties of a major accident may have very different levels of health effect, dependent on routes and duration of exposure, and individual susceptibilities;

(d) workers, emergency response and NHS personnel will themselves be at risk through contact with chemically contaminated casualties. However, the appropriate use of personal protective equipment will minimise the risks of contamination;

(e) the capacity of hospitals to handle contaminated casualties is limited. Mishandling of early cases may spread contamination and put facilities out of action;

(f) hospitals and the roads leading to the hospitals may lie in the path of a chemical plume (eg a visible or measurable discharge);

(g) dispersed populations may be affected through the contamination of water supplies or the food chain;

(h) accidents cause fear, and sometimes anxiety in populations, which may dramatically increase the number of referrals to hospitals and general practitioners, and overwhelm telephone helplines; and

(i) public concern, and the concerns of workers and response personnel, may extend beyond the acute phase to potential long-term effects on human health, such as cancers and congenital malformations, and to psychosomatic phenomena.

NHS roles and responsibilities

126 Operators and local authorities need to be aware of the roles and responsibilities placed on different parts of the NHS by the United Kingdom (UK) Government Health Departments (for a fuller account, please refer to section 8 of *Planning for major incidents: the NHS guidance* or part 2 of *A manual of guidance responding to emergencies - guidance for the NHS in Scotland)*. The key responsibilities of each part are as follows:

(a) *Health authorities in England and Wales, and health boards in Scotland* - are responsible for ensuring that satisfactory arrangements are in place for handling the public health and health care aspects of the response to a major accident.

(b) *Acute hospital trusts* - are responsible for ensuring that satisfactory arrangements are in place for providing health care to the casualties of a major accident.

(c) *Ambulance trusts* - are responsible for ensuring that satisfactory arrangements are in place for providing health care to the

casualties at, and in transit from, the scene of a major accident.

(d) *General practitioners/community health trusts* - are responsible for ensuring that satisfactory arrangements are in place for providing health care to the casualties of a major accident, and with providing support and aftercare to the affected populations.

(e) *Regional offices of the NHS in England* - are responsible for advising on the leadership and co-ordination arrangements for the NHS response to a major accident, where more than one health authority is involved or where the number of casualties dictates special provision.

(f) *National Focus for Work on Response to Chemical Accidents* - is responsible for alerting and briefing the Department of Health, Welsh Office, and the Scottish Office Department of Health on the public health aspects of a major accident, and for the national co-ordination of public health activity, where appropriate.

General principles

127 In developing the public health related components of their respective plans and in seeking to achieve integrated emergency management, operators and local authorities need to consult with health authorities and ambulance trusts, and to jointly agree respective roles and responsibilities. Health authorities will also consult, or facilitate consultation with, the appropriate hospital and emergency units and acute hospital trusts.

128 Procedures also need to be considered and jointly agreed for activating the various component parts of the NHS response. This includes identifying the relevant post holders from each authority or trust to attend strategic, tactical and operational controls, where appropriate. It may be prudent for health authorities to consider strategies and back-up plans if one health authority became overwhelmed by the number of casualties arising from an incident.

129 The public health aspects of a major accident involving dangerous substances will

invariably continue after the joint command and control structure of the emergency services has been stood down.

130   Certain hazardous chemical substances may give rise to delayed harmful effects following the initial exposure, even after rapid decontamination has taken place. These effects may not be confined to known victims of chemical exposure, but may also affect rescuers and those who provide first aid, advanced life support, general treatment and nursing care to casualties. In addition, people who have not apparently been exposed to any substances associated with the incident, for example evacuees, may also show delayed signs or symptoms. All medical emergency response services need to include in their emergency plans, instructions and procedures that all initial emergency response and subsequent care personnel should be alert to the possibility of delayed signs and symptoms.

Availability of equipment, supplies and facilities

131   Operators are required to carry out periodic safety assessments on the nature and magnitude of possible accident scenarios present at COMAH sites, including (if appropriate) the chemicals likely to be released and the potential injuries that may be caused. The sharing of this information by the operators will help health authorities, acute hospital trusts and ambulance trusts. They will be better placed to ensure the immediate availability of the various emergency medical and public health resources needed (including personnel, equipment, supplies, facilities and funds) to respond to different types of accidents and to the range of possible casualties. For example, they will be able to match supplies of up-to-date stocks of antidotes with the presence of hazardous substances at particular sites, and to determine the most suitable holding locations.

Liaison

132   Operators and local authorities need to work closely with health authorities and ambulance trusts, as well as with the emergency services, government agencies and other key organisations, in considering when and where decontamination of casualties and response personnel should take place; and in determining the level of personal protective equipment needed for use by response and decontamination personnel.

133   More specifically, local authorities need to talk with health authorities and the relevant voluntary aid societies, about including arrangements in their off-site plans for managing the health care needs of individuals who have been evacuated. This would include, for example, access to routine medications if the evacuation is prolonged, and the provision of services to support people suffering from stress-related conditions as a result of the incident.

Specialist sources of advice and expertise

134   Operators and local authorities should be aware of the sources of specialist advice and expertise available to NHS personnel involved in the management of major accidents. Conversely, the NHS needs to be aware that the chemical industry has specialist knowledge and expertise on the effects of the chemicals they handle. The sources of advice available to NHS personnel include:

(a)   *National Poisons Information Service Centres* - who provide advice to the NHS 24 hours-a-day, 365 days-a-year on the hazardous (or otherwise) nature of the chemicals involved in an accident and on clinical management following exposure;

(b)   *Regional Service Provider Units (RSPUs)* - who are contracted by health authorities to support them with the public health, environmental, scientific, toxicological and epidemiological aspects of chemical accidents;

(c)   *National Focus for Work on Response to Chemical Incidents* - fulfils the roles detailed in paragraph 126, and works closely with the RSPUs to ensure that there is consistency of advice, particularly in relation to accidents with potential cross-boundary effects;

(d)   *Health Advisory Group on Chemical Contamination Incidents (HAGCCI)* - which is activated, where appropriate, by the National Focus. HAGCCI was established by the Department of Health in 1991 to act as an independent, authoritative source of advice to health authorities and the Chief Medical Officers of England, Wales and Scotland on the human health aspects of chemical accidents.

Assessing the public health aspects of chemical accidents

135   Under *Planning for major incidents: the NHS guidance*, and in the equivalent Scottish guidance for health boards, the essential response actions placed on health authorities include:

(a)   evaluating the risk to the health of the public in the light of the available toxicological data on the chemical(s) released, the results of biological and environmental sampling, the epidemiological findings, and the receipt of appropriate specialist advice and support; and

(b)   advising on the measures needed to limit or prevent further exposure of the public to the chemicals released in any major accident.

Epidemiological follow-up

136   For many chemicals, limited information is available regarding their effects on human health. The short-term and long-term follow-up of people who may have been exposed to chemicals during an accident can therefore be useful from both a therapeutic and a scientific viewpoint. However, health authorities face a dilemma. On the one hand, follow-up studies may be time-consuming, expensive, and often uninformative. They may offer little prospect of health gain, and may even induce morbidity, by raising unwarranted fears (and litigation) in the exposed population. On the other hand, without such studies, it is often easy to miss important health problems arising from an accident, especially if these commence later, or are non-specific or not obvious consequences of the exposure.

137   Advance consideration must therefore be given to the decision-making processes which will need to be rapidly effected following any major accident in determining whether such follow-up studies are warranted. This needs to include liaison with the operator in terms of the potential follow-up of exposed workers, and with the emergency services who may have concerns regarding their own personnel.

Environmental aspects of major accidents

General principles

138   COMAH regards all major accidents as having equal status whether their effects are primarily on people or on the environment. Consequently there is a need to take account of the environment in both on-site and off-site emergency plans drawn up under COMAH.

What is a major accident?

139   Regulation 2 of COMAH details a number of definitions. These include 'what is a major accident'. This is defined as:

> *an occurrence (including in particular, a major emission, fire or explosion) resulting from uncontrolled developments in the course of the operation of any establishment and leading to serious danger to human health or the environment, immediate or delayed, inside or outside the establishment, and involving one or more dangerous substances.*
>
> *Regulations*

140   Further information on details of hazardous events can be found in Appendix 1.

What is the environment?

141   In terms of COMAH, the 'environment' comprises built features, air, water, soil, flora and fauna. This includes those featues which have protected, designated or controlled status, such as controlled waters, any sensitive land within the site boundaries, protected buildings and monuments, protected ecological species, and protected habitats or designated areas. An accident is considered to be major if it causes permanent or long-term damage to a particular unique, rare or otherwise valued component of the built or natural environment, or if there is widespread environmental loss, contamination or damage. The effect of an accident on the natural environment may be direct or indirect, immediate or delayed, temporary or persistent.

142   Consequently, the indirect effects of an accident need to be contemplated as well as the more obvious ones. Food and agriculture, together with other features such as sewage and water treatment works, need consideration.

Emergency planning for the environment

143   The objectives of emergency plans for COMAH establishments are listed in paragraph 19. To meet these objectives for the environment, emergency plans need to consider:

(a)   possible accident scenarios;

(b)   the predicted environmental effects of accidents;

(c)   implementation of specific measures to protect the environment;

(d)   liaison with other environmental organisations and the public; and

(e)   environmental clean-up and restoration.

144   The safety report should contain much of the information required for planning purposes, and it will have been assessed by the competent

authority (HSE and EA or SEPA). However, the local authority will consult with the appropriate environment agency before the off-site emergency plan is finalised.

Assessing the environmental effects of accidents

145   The effects of an accident on the environment depend upon a number of factors particular to the accident. Operators of COMAH establishments should have carried out a detailed environmental risk assessment as part of the safety report. Emergency planners can use this information to help develop on-site and off-site emergency plans. The aim of the risk assessment is to show which hazards and events contribute to the risks to the environment from an accident at the establishment. This will allow prioritisation of effort in managing these risks. The depth of each assessment should be proportional to the risk posed by the establishment.

146   Risk assessments should consider:

(a)   the substances and processes present at the establishment;

(b)   the pathways of contamination from the establishment to the environment; and

(c)   the location of establishments in relation to environmental features.

These considerations are expanded in the following paragraphs. Further guidance on interpreting major accidents to the environment is contained in Department of the Environment, Transport and the Regions (DETR) guidance notes for COMAH establishments.[8]

Nature of the pollutant

147   In the case of major accidents, the nature of any pollution is determined by the activities on the establishment and by the dangerous substances present or released in the event of an accident. Emergency plans should concentrate on those events and substances most likely to cause damage to the environment.

148   Not all emissions to the environment cause damage. It is important to know the toxicity and behaviour of any chemical that might be released into the environment. Some apparently harmless substances can have a damaging effect on the

environment, for example milk can damage watercourses as a result of its very high oxygen demand. The degree of persistence of any material that reaches the environment is also likely to be of significance. A material that degrades very rapidly to harmless chemicals is less likely to have a serious effect than one that is persistent and has toxic characteristics. Ecotoxicological information on substances on the establishment should be obtained. This can help highlight those chemicals that would pose higher risks to the environment should there be an accident. Information on the ecotoxicity of substances can be obtained from a variety of sources, such as:

(a)   Chemicals (Hazard Information and Packaging for Supply) Regulations (CHIP) information from HSE;[9]

(b)   Ecotoxicology and Hazardous Substances National Centre at EA; and

(c)   Water Research Centre - National Centre of Ecotoxicity.

Pathways to the environment

149   To assess the areas that might be affected in the event of an accident, all possible pathways by which contaminants can reach the environment should be examined. The two main pathways for environmental contamination are by air and water. Contaminants may also percolate through the soil.

150   The effects caused by airborne pollutants can cover a wide area and are more difficult to predict and control than pollutants released into water. Precipitation may be in dry ash form, or dissolved in rain, snow, etc. The affected area will depend on weather conditions. The Meteorological Office can usually supply information on wind speed and direction in order to help define the area most likely to be affected.

151   Surface run-off into sewers (foul and surface water), drains, discharge pipes and watercourses causes downstream effects, potentially carrying contaminants a long way from the immediate area, and possibly reaching groundwater. The importance of this vector for pollution depends on the speed and flow of nearby watercourses, and on the nature of the local drainage system.

The local environment

152   In preparing an emergency plan to protect the environment, it is most important to characterise the features of the environment around the establishment. Determination of particularly important or sensitive areas will identify those areas for which particular protective measures may have to be implemented.

153   This does not necessarily require a detailed ecological audit. A preliminary study could be used to categorise broad features of land use in the area, for example, residential, agricultural, fisheries, water organisations, or woodland. Local nature conservation agencies, EA or SEPA and planning authorities should hold most of this information. Nevertheless some form of environmental survey may be needed, and EA or SEPA can advise on this.

154   Any environmentally sensitive areas within range of the establishment need to be identified. In the case of rivers and aquatic sites of special scientific interest (SSSIs), sensitive areas put at risk by an accident may be some distance from the establishment. Environmentally sensitive areas might include those with statutory protection such as:

(a)   SSSIs;

(b)   areas of outstanding natural beauty;

(c)   listed buildings;

(d)   ancient monuments;

(e)   trees protected by tree preservation orders;

(f)   groundwater protection zones; and

(g)   water abstraction points or other areas of environmental importance, such as:

    (i)   salmonid rivers;

    (ii) local amenity areas;

    (iii) zoned open space.

155   The specific sensitivity of each SSSI needs to be determined. An SSSI might support a particular habitat type or species that is especially susceptible to some forms of pollution. This information can be obtained from the local office of the relevant statutory nature conservation agency and EA or SEPA. Information on the location of important features relevant to the water industry can be obtained from the relevant Agency (EA or SEPA). Information on important parts of the built heritage may be obtained from the relevant country heritage agency. Other nearby areas may be of importance to the local community, and information can be obtained from the local authority and from local conservation or special interest groups.

Identification of measures to protect the environment

156   The emergency plans should identify specific actions and measures needed to prevent and to mitigate the impact to the environment from an accident. By considering the need for specific actions and measures in advance, informed decisions can be made that will help maximise the level of protection afforded to the environment by the plans. Some level of environmental damage may be inevitable, but it is vital to think through which, of a range of possible actions and measures to control an accident, will cause the least harm to the environment, and also protect especially vulnerable components. All planned decisions and actions need to be agreed and rehearsed in advance with the relevant organisations. Obviously it is important to recognise that the options considered should not conflict with measures to protect human health.

Liaison

157   It is important that the environmental protection aspects of emergency plans are agreed with all parties involved in the response to the accident or with responsibility for any area, habitat, species or building likely to be affected.

158   The fire service needs to know where sensitive water supplies are: to avoid drawing excessively from them in putting out any fire, and to help avoid pollution of water through run-off contaminated water. If there are any specific mitigation measures in place on the establishment for containing this firewater, the fire service should be aware of them so that they can be used

effectively. The fire service may also have anti-pollution equipment available for use.

159   Liaison with EA or SEPA is needed to establish the water quality in local watercourses, water abstraction points, the presence of aquifers and the vulnerability of these features to pollution. The Agencies (EA and SEPA) also have emergency response arrangements to prevent contamination dispersion. Measures in their plans may include booming off oil slicks, soaking up contaminants and diverting watercourses. The Agencies will also liaise with the water companies/authorities and operators to avoid damage to water and sewerage installations. Liaison and co-ordination with the Agencies may help in preventing adverse impacts. In the event of a very toxic release, the local public health official or environmental protection officer should be contacted. Many fire brigades act on behalf of the Agencies in the initial response to incidents to prevent environmental damage, so the emergency services and/or the local authority may contact water companies/authorities direct.

160   Liaison with the relevant country nature conservation agency (Scottish Natural Heritage, Countryside Council for Wales, or English Nature) helps to identify important areas and those sensitive to pollution. Liaison with the relevant built heritage agencies (English Heritage, Historic Scotland, Royal Commission on Ancient and Historical Monuments for Scotland (RCAHMS), and Royal Commission on Ancient and Historical Monuments for Wales (RCAHMW)) and the National Trust and others may be needed to help identify any historic sites at risk. Liaison between operators, local authorities and landowners is also crucial.

Environmental clean-up and restoration

161   One requirement of COMAH is that the on-site and off-site emergency plans provide for the clean-up and restoration of the environment after an accident. The remedial measures should be proportional to the amount of harm caused by the accident, and to the likely level of continuing harm to people and the environment. The operator has a duty to take remedial measures to mitigate the effects of major accidents under regulation 4 of COMAH and under other environmental legislation such as the Water Resources Act 1991 and the Wildlife and Countryside Act 1981.

162   Emergency plans may consider and identify initiating procedures, contractors and where appropriate, arrangements for:

(a)   removing contaminated soil and debris;

(b)   restricting foodstuffs (including those grown at home);

(c)   restricting access to areas;

(d)   restocking watercourses, lakes, woods, etc; and

(e)   remedial action on surface and groundwater supplies.

163   These are examples and should not be considered a definitive list. On-site emergency plans should consider removing contaminated soil and debris, whereas off-site plans may need to consider many more areas. Lead agencies for each of these arrangements need to be identified.

164   Some remedial measures and restoration arrangements may be needed urgently after the accident (for example, access restriction), whereas others can wait until an environmental impact assessment has taken place.

165   Contaminated areas, even on site, can pose a continuing threat to the environment after an accident. Clean-up could require the removal or cleansing of soil, ashes may need containing to ensure that they cannot blow away, and drums of chemicals may need to be labelled and disposed of by licensed disposal contractors. Contaminated water held in bunds or storage may need to be removed and processed to make safe and non-toxic.

166   Remedial work may involve replacing contaminated soil with clean soil, along with replanting vegetation. Fish populations in rivers and watercourses may require restocking. In severe cases, long-term projects may be required to rehabilitate areas and restore habitats.

167   The extent of remedial action covered by off-site emergency plans should take account of the particular environmental hazards associated with the operations carried out on the establishment and the specific off-site environmental conditions. This might involve: neutralising, removing and disposing of chemical

contaminants; removing dead animals, plants or contaminated soil; re-introducing species; repairing damaged parts of the built environment; etc.

168   There are a number of environmental consultants who specialise in restorating contaminated land. In the case of oil spills, consultants should have British Oil Spill Control Agency (BOSCA) accreditation. If an important site for nature conservation is damaged, then full liaison should occur with the relevant country nature conservation agency. Emergency plans can usefully include a list of specialist contacts for both clean-up and remedial measures, but it may be more appropriate to ensure that the administrative structures and arrangements are in place to facilitate rapid clean-up in case this is needed after an accident.

169   Repairing the damage to buildings should be considered in consultation with local authorities and the built heritage agencies.

Food and agricultural effects

170   The immediate actions to safeguard the public food supply following an accident rest with various government departments, and this section summarises their key roles.

171   A chemical release during an accident may lead to local contamination of the food chain, usually through direct deposition onto pasture or crops from aerial releases. In some cases, this may occur from uptake into plants through contaminated water. When food or food animals

become contaminated, the assessment of the potential risk to people is the responsibility of: the Department of Health and Ministry of Agriculture, Fisheries, and Food in England; the Scottish Office Agriculture, Environment and Fisheries Department in Scotland; the Welsh Office, Agriculture Department in Wales.

172   Information on the extent and nature of the problem is gathered through these government departments' regional contacts. Investigation may involve taking blood samples where animals have been exposed, or sampling suspect food for laboratory analysis. Local agricultural department officials and environmental health officers will generally obtain information on an accident from the emergency services, rather than from operators directly.

173   Once the extent of any problem has been identified, control over the entry of affected foods into the food chain, eg through the contamination of crops or grazing land, may be via voluntary restrictions on farmers, or action by local councils. Where this is inadequate, there are emergency powers which government can use immediately (Part 1 of the Food and Environment Protection Act 1985, and section 13 of the Food Safety Act 1990).

174   The agriculture and health departments would take responsibility for providing information of a food emergency to the public and media, and this would take place through their press offices or emergency centres, as well as through regional offices and local environmental health departments.

Training and testing

Training

175 The COMAH safety report requires evidence that the operator's safety management system contains suitable arrangements for training individuals on the establishment in emergency response. The type of training required depends upon the role of the individual in the event of an emergency. This should cover members of staff with a particular role in the emergency response, as well as other members of staff, contractors and visitors to the establishment.

176 The training should be kept up to date as appropriate, with suitable refresher training. The participation in the testing of an emergency plan is not solely a training exercise. All those involved in testing emergency plans should have had some previous training to introduce them to their role in an emergency (even if this is only to follow instructions and to go inside). All relevant staff from every shift, in all the relevant organisations, should receive full training in their expected response in the event of an emergency. The aims and objectives of training should always be made clear at the outset. The effectiveness of the training should be reviewed and evaluated.

Testing

177 Emergency plans prepared to meet the requirements of COMAH should be tested at least once every three years. This applies to both on-site and off-site emergency plans, and effectively sets a minimum standard.

178 This testing is carried out to give confidence that the plans are accurate, complete and practicable. It should be able to show that people following the emergency plan could cope with the range of accidents that could occur. The testing should give an indication of the conditions that may exist on and off the establishment in the event of an emergency. It should also show that the plan would work as proposed: controlling and mitigating the effects of an accident; communicating the necessary information; and initiating the measures which should lead to the necessary restoration of the environment.

179 *Testing should be based on an accident scenario identified in the safety report as being reasonably foreseeable. Tests should address the response during the initial emergency phase, which is usually the first few hours after the accident occurs. This is the phase of an accident response when key decisions, which will greatly affect the success of any mitigation measures, must be made under considerable pressure and within a short period of time. Therefore, this is where a detailed understanding of the likely sequence of events and appropriate countermeasures is of great benefit.*

180 It is important that the simple issues of the emergency response are not overlooked by over-concentration on the more complex areas. The overall testing regime should consider, over a period of time, the full range of hazards capable of producing a major accident, not just the most significant hazards. There is also the option of including testing of later phases of an emergency,

following on from the initial stage of the clean-up and restoration phase. This could be achieved by, for example, extending a table-top exercise.

181 Testing on-site and off-site emergency plans (or parts of plans) at the same time can produce considerable benefits. These benefits include ensuring that both emergency plans work effectively together, and offering potential financial savings by avoiding duplicate testing. For example, the external agencies' roles in mitigation, both on-site and off-site, are described only in the off-site emergency plan; there is no such reference in the on-site plan. Exercising this part of the off-site emergency plan with the on-site emergency plan can test the effective co-ordination of all emergency response personnel handling a major accident on the site. Agreement needs to be made on the overall objectives of the testing and the most appropriate route to reach these objectives.

Objectives of testing

182 The objective of testing the emergency plan should be to give confidence in the following constituents of the plan:

(a) the completeness, consistency and accuracy of the emergency plan and other documentation used by organisations responding to an emergency;

(b) the adequacy of the equipment and facilities, and their operability, especially under emergency conditions; and

(c) the competence of staff to carry out the duties identified for them in the plan, and their use of the equipment and facilities.

183 The overall testing regime for on-site and off-site emergency plans would be expected to examine the following aspects of the emergency response:

(a) activating the emergency plan and notifying the participants:

   (i) alerting emergency services;

   (ii) sounding alarms; and

   (iii) mobilising establishment personnel identified in the emergency plan as

having a role to play in the event of an emergency.

(b) establishing an on-site emergency control centre (ECC)

establishing a suitable place from where the on-site response to the emergency can be directed and co-ordinated as required by the on-site emergency plan, within a suitable time. (Also considering the ability to establish an alternative on-site ECC in some tests, to demonstrate the ability to operate when the designated on-site ECC is untenable.)

(c) establishing an off-site ECC

establishing a suitable place from where the off-site response to the emergency can be directed and co-ordinated, which may be through a strategic co-ordinating group.

(d) supplying information to the ECC

demonstrating that information from the participating organisations can be supplied promptly and accurately to the ECC, so that those at the centre have access to an up-to-date picture of the emergency and the response to it, and from which they can base their decision making.

(e) communicating within the ECC

demonstrating that the necessary information is exchanged and disseminated among all the parties with a role to play at the ECC, and is in a form that can be understood and assimilated.

(f) team working

demonstrating the ability of participating organisations to work together, using the available information to develop the response to the emergency.

(g) decision making

demonstrating that advice is provided by all participating organisations to allow rational decisions to be made, which can be implemented.

(h)   communication and public information

   (i)   demonstrating that information on the emergency, and the response to it, is passed to all participating organisations and to the appropriate media;

   (ii)   the demonstration should include preparing briefs for the media and should sometimes include establishing a media briefing centre. In addition, consideration should be given as to the effect of the media in the event of an emergency, and the ability of the ECC to make information available for handling their enquiries.

(i)   equipment and facilities

   demonstrating that the equipment identified as having a role in the response to an emergency is operational, and that participants are able to use it. Also, demonstrating the operability of the ECC and the equipment associated with it.

Methods of training and testing

184   Exercises to test on-site and off-site emergency plans, and which form part of the ongoing training of key personnel in preparation for dealing with an emergency, can take a number of forms. These will fulfil different functions within the overall requirements. These exercises include:

(a)   drills

   testing a specific and relatively simple aspect of the emergency plan in isolation. Examples are: fire drills; alarm testing; evacuation; roll call and searching; cascade telephone calls; spillage control and recovery;

(b)   seminar exercises

   training staff and developing emergency plans. They facilitate discussion about the different organisations' responses in particular circumstances during an emergency;

(c)   walk-through exercises

   training staff or developing emergency plans. The emergency response is 'walked through', including visiting appropriate facilities such as ECCs;

(d)   table-top exercises

   allowing information exchange and dissemination between organisations at the ECC, together with decision making, to be tested. They are carried out in relation to a model, plans or photographs to depict the establishment. They could involve using information technology or virtual reality systems;

(e)   control post exercises

   testing the communication arrangements during an emergency, with participating organisations located where they would be during an emergency;

(f)   live exercises

   fully testing some or all aspects of the emergency plan for the on-site and off-site response.

185   Further information on different types of emergency exercises can be found in the Home Office publication *The exercise planners guide*.[10]

186   There are many different ways, using different combinations of the tests described in paragraph 184, to address the elements of emergency plans that require testing (see paragraphs 182 and 183). For example, carrying out a live exercise of one of the major accidents identified in the safety report would greatly increase the confidence in the ability of the emergency plan to function adequately in the event of an accident. However, it would be an enormous burden on all those involved if this was considered the only way of testing emergency plans.

187   It is important to draw up a programme of emergency plan tests, prepared jointly and agreed by all the agencies expected to participate. This produces a high level of confidence in the plan without overburdening the operator and the other organisations responding to the emergency.

188   A single test can address aspects for more than one installation within an establishment, or more than one establishment within a local authority area, which can lead to considerable economies of scale. There is also the option to test on-site and off-site plans at the same time.

189   The aims and objectives of testing emergency plans should always be made clear at the outset (both at the planning stage and on the day). The lessons learned should be passed to all the stakeholders involved at a local level, and nationally, if appropriate, eg by sending reports to the competent authority or Home Office.

190   Sharing the lessons learned is especially important in the case where a single test is used to demonstrate the effectiveness of the emergency plan for more than one installation or establishment. If this approach is adopted, there may be the need for additional testing of specific aspects of the emergency response for individual installations or establishments. It is recommended that records are kept of tests carried out under a regime of this kind, to provide audit trails to show that the relevant components of the emergency plan have been tested during the three year period.

Evaluation

191   For organisations to get the most out of their participation in emergency plan tests, it is important to evaluate the lessons learned, to determine whether modifications are required to the emergency plan and to promote good practice. With the different organisations involved in emergency plan tests, there will be more than one method for evaluating the effectiveness of the emergency plan, and each organisation may want to establish its own self-evaluation criteria relevant to its own response. For example, organisations may want to set quantitative measures like timeliness of response, or subjective measures for quality of performance.

192   This evaluation process needs to include the dissemination of information and the lessons learned, as appropriate, to the relevant response organisations who need to be kept informed of progress on any actions to amend emergency plan responses. This will also cover any recommendations arising from the testing and the progress of actions. This evaluation should also cover the need to revise information to the public, if appropriate.

193   Effective evaluation gives assurance to operators and to participating organisations that the arrangements that they have in place for dealing with an emergency are effective and will work adequately in the event of an accident.

194   Techniques are available to record the response of key players during an exercise to allow some comparison of the effectiveness of emergency plans. These techniques can also be used to study the effectiveness of the training of the decision makers in emergency response.

Informing the public

195   When alarms are being tested, or when exercises are being carried out of the on-site or off-site emergency response, there will be understandable concern from those in the vicinity of the establishment. They will hear alarms and be aware of the movement of emergency service vehicles. It is good practice to inform those in the vicinity of the establishment that such testing is taking place. It also helps to inform the emergency services' call centres that such testing or exercising is taking place so that they can field calls from concerned neighbours, and hopefully allay any unnecessary fears. It may be appropriate for the operator to prepare a briefing for the media to handle press enquiries when tests or exercises of this kind are planned, so that they can respond in a proactive and informative manner. The later chapters on 'Informing and warning the public' and 'Working with the media' contain more information.

Initiation of emergency plans

196 COMAH regulation 12 requires that the person who has prepared an emergency plan takes reasonable steps to ensure it is put into effect without delay when:

(a) a major accident occurs; or

(b) an uncontrolled event occurs which could reasonably be expected to lead to a major accident.

197 The operator and the local authority discharge this duty, placed on them as corporate organisations under regulation 12, by producing emergency plans which have adequate arrangements in place to initiate the plans. The responsibilities of the operator and the local authority are met if there are robust arrangements in place for ensuring that, under all reasonably foreseeable circumstances, the plan will be initiated to respond to a major hazard accident.

198 The emergency plan should identify who has the responsibility for initiating the emergency plan and when this should be done. The plan should also include when the emergency services should be alerted to ensure that no unnecessary delays occur which could have serious consequences.

199 The operator and the emergency services should agree who has authority to activate any off-site siren or other means of warning the public that an accident has occurred, and when this should happen. This should be agreed while developing the emergency plan, to avoid unnecessary delays during the response to an emergency. Under most circumstances, it is appropriate to identify an employee of the operator of the establishment (by name or position) in the emergency plan as having the responsibility for sounding any off-site alarm. However, in some circumstances, for example on an establishment not attended around the clock, it may be more appropriate if this function is carried out by the first emergency member of the external fire service to arrive at the establishment.

Review and revision

200 Regulation 11 of COMAH requires that at least once every three years the on-site and the off-site emergency plans for a top-tier COMAH establishment should be reviewed, and where necessary revised.

201 In this context, reviewing the emergency plan is considered to be a fundamental process, examining the adequacy and the effectiveness of the components of the emergency plan and how they function together. The review process should take into account:

(a) all material changes in the activity of the establishment;

(b) any changes in the emergency services relevant to the operation of the plan;

(c) advances in technical knowledge, for example new and more effective means of mitigation;

(d) changes in staffing resources including contractors;

(e) knowledge gained as a result of major accidents either on site or elsewhere; and

(f) lessons learned during the testing of emergency plans.

202 For this to take place effectively there has to be open communication between the operator, local authority and emergency services. All appropriate changes which may affect the emergency response should be communicated to the other parties.

203 A review of the on-site and the off-site emergency plans should also take place following any significant modifications to the establishment or any other significant changes. Under these circumstances, the operator and local authority should not wait until the three year review required by COMAH is due.

204 Review and revision are considered to be a separate requirement from the updating of emergency plans, which is an ongoing process. The updating is carried out to reflect any changes in the practical details of the emergency response arrangements, for example changes in the responding organisations' communication arrangements or in the available mitigation equipment. Some emergency plans may name the personnel who have responsibility for initiating the emergency response or for liaising with the local authority when preparing the off-site emergency plan. In these cases, the updating should include changing the names as appropriate, rather than waiting for the three yearly review of the plans. It is recommended that the names and telephone numbers of authorised personnel are included in the annexes of emergency plans; this facilitates making any changes.

205 One of the principal inputs to the process of reviewing the emergency plans comes from the results of testing emergency plans, as discussed in the earlier chapter on 'Training and testing'. Before testing, objectives should be set for all aspects of exercising an emergency plan. After the test, the review should concentrate on areas where the objectives were not met (see paragraphs 189-194 for further details). The

recommendations from reviews and tests of the emergency plans should be logged, and action taken to address each recommendation. The revisions to emergency plans should be actioned in a timely manner, and the progress monitored. For off-site emergency plans, this would be done through the local emergency planning consultative group.

Informing and warning the public

Informing the public

206   COMAH requires the operator to provide appropriate information to people within the public information zone. The public information zone is the area where people are liable to be affected by a major accident. This is determined by the competent authority taking account of the likelihood and possible effects of a major accident at the establishment. The public information zone does not extend to where a major accident might affect the environment alone.

207   Schedule 6 of COMAH details the information that must be provided, but this is the minimum information and operators are free to provide more if they wish. Further details can be found on regulation 14, provision of information to the public, in the guidance on COMAH.

208   The importance of effectively communicating information to children as well as adults should be borne in mind, for example by the development of educational packages in schools and colleges, and the use of videos. In some locations there is the need to provide translations of the information into other languages. Publicising the information can take a variety of forms, which should be readily accessible and durable. This could include combining the information into a wall calendar, although this then requires annual distribution of the information.

209   Further details on informing the public about test exercises or alarm tests are given in paragraph 195.

Warning the public

210   There should be an effective method for warning the public within the public information zone of a major accident (see paragraphs 116 and 218, and the guidance on COMAH on Schedule 6 for further details). In addition, people located outside the public information zone also have information needs which should be met by the emergency plans. Unless arrangements are made to reassure the public outside the public information zone, there may be unnecessary alarm. This increases the risk of important telephone links being jammed, if the public is seeking information while an incident is ongoing.

Working with the media

211   In the event of a major accident there are two functions that are carried out by the media:

(a)   they gather information for news stories; and

(b)   they act as a route to broadcast important information to those who may be affected in the vicinity of the accident.

News gathering

212   The first role of the media cannot be ignored in emergency planning. If the needs of the media to collect information are not met, it may be more difficult to use them to inform the public. An on-site tactical or operational group, or an off-site strategic co-ordinating group, should identify an appropriate person to act as a co-ordinator for working with the media. This should be included in both the on-site and off-site emergency plans so that all agencies are clear about who will act as the media co-ordinator. This person should be a representative of one of the key responding organisations and should be appropriately trained for working closely with the media. A suitable person could be a police or fire service press officer.

213   It will often be appropriate to establish a media briefing centre, where information agreed by the strategic co-ordinating group can be released, and where representatives of the operator and the responding organisations can give interviews and press conferences. Those who may need to attend a press conference, or be interviewed, should receive appropriate training for working with the media, and they should be adequately briefed on the development of the accident. Press officers from all the responding agencies may be required at the media briefing centre along with the operator's representatives. Information released to the media by the operator or any of the responding organisations should be copied to the press officers of all the other organisations. This ensures that all the organisations dealing with the media are aware of what other information has been made available.

214   Although not mandatory, it is recommended that certain information is prepared in advance, for distribution in the event of an emergency, for example on the work carried out on the establishment, and background information on the company and on the local area. Such information will be required rapidly by media representatives. Television journalists will appreciate the availability of broadcast quality video with appropriate footage of the establishment and the work carried out. This will give operators background material from which to provide accident-specific information.

215   It is important that all the information passed to the media during an accident is accurate and consistent, and not based on speculation. If possible, a steady stream of appropriate information should be released to the media after due liaison with the other involved parties. This may be up-to-date information on the developing accident, supported by background briefing on the nature of the chemical released (if known), on the company and on the establishment.

216 If it is safe and practicable to do so, it may be appropriate to establish a media point within sight of the establishment to enable appropriate footage and photographs of the response to the accident to be taken. This may reduce the risk of photographers and camera crews attempting to get close to the developing incident and putting themselves at risk.

217 Any potential misunderstanding between the media and an operator can be reduced if steps are taken to establish some mutual understanding. If this is done in advance of any accident occurring, then in the event of an incident, the media should have some understanding of the work carried out on the establishment, the risks associated with the work, the controls in place to manage those risks and the existence of appropriate emergency response arrangements. The operator should in return understand the need of the media to gather information for reporting rapidly and accurately to the public on the accident and its implications.

Broadcasting emergency information

218 The broadcasting media, especially local radio stations, have another role in the event of an accident which is to inform the public, including details of what to do for their own safety. People living in the vicinity of the establishment will have received prior information from the operator, and this may make a number of recommendations, in the event of residents becoming aware of an incident at the operator's establishment. These recommendations may include going indoors, shutting doors and windows, and tuning in to a local radio station (such information may be reinforced by the use of local slogans, eg the Cheshire Fire Brigade's 'Go in, Stay in, Tune in'). When this is the case, arrangements should be made between the emergency services, the operator and the local radio stations. These should cover how the radio stations are informed that an accident has happened, what information needs to be given to the public, how the information is updated and how the all-clear is given. They should also consider what information will be needed to reassure members of the public who become aware of the incident, but are in no danger themselves.

Appendix 1: Hazardous events

Hazardous events may affect people, and operators should co-operate with local authorities, emergency services and other agencies to develop appropriate strategies to protect people from the effects of such events. Examples of possible emergency responses to deal with particular hazardous events are given in the following paragraphs.

Flammable releases

(a) A release of flammable material may result in fire or explosion. The consequences depend upon the nature of the material released, the quantity released, whether it is ignited, and the time between release and any ignition. If the release is a volatile liquid or a gas and it is not ignited immediately, it will form a cloud which may disperse over a large distance. The dispersing cloud will become diluted with air as it moves away from the point of release. Eventually its concentration will fall below the substance's lower flammable limit, and so no longer present a fire hazard. The distance over which such a release may disperse depends upon the quantity, properties and state of the material, the nature of the release and the prevailing weather conditions. The concentrations in the dispersing cloud may be estimated using appropriate computer programs which combine a mathematical model of a physical description of cloud behaviour with data collected from experiments and incidents.

(b) If a developed cloud is ignited, it may burn as a flash fire back to the point of failure. If a release from a broken pipe, leaking flange or a hole in a vessel is ignited immediately, it may burn as a jet fire or a pool fire. Models are available for estimating the quantity of material released over time, and the size and thermal radiation from jet fires and pool fires.

(c) Vapour cloud explosions following a massive release of a gas or volatile liquid, and boiling liquid expanding vapour cloud explosions (BLEVEs), are low frequency, high consequence events. These may occur with certain flammable fluids under certain accident conditions. Methods are available for estimating the size of a vapour cloud explosion or BLEVE fireball, the thermal radiation consequences and the levels of blast over-pressure.

(d) There is a considerable range of possible accident scenarios involving the release of flammable materials which will have considerably different consequences and therefore need different planned emergency responses. Examples may be:

(i) *A major fire, but with no danger of an explosion, for example a fire in a none crude oil storage tank*
The hazards would be high levels of thermal radiation and smoke for a long duration. Evacuation may be required from buildings close to the establishment and directly exposed to severe thermal radiation. In addition, it

may be necessary to evacuate areas severely affected by smoke.

(ii) *A major full surface fire in a large crude oil storage tank*
There is the potential for a boil over to occur, which could propel the burning tank contents upwards and outwards for up to ten times the diameter of the tank involved, whether or not fire fighting is taking place. The evacuation of all non-essential personnel from within the area noted, and arrangements to deal with any possible escalation, should be included in any plans.

(iii) *A fire threatening a major item of plant or a storage tank containing hazardous materials*
The safety report should include an assessment of the possible consequences of such an event, and it should identify the area that may need to be evacuated. The planned response should give appropriate consideration to the assessment of the consequences.

(iv) *A fire threatening a major item of plant that develops too quickly to allow evacuation*
Under these circumstances, the best advice for those in the vicinity may be to remain indoors away from windows and shielded from line of sight of the fire. There may be significant risks in attempting to evacuate if a BLEVE or fireball could occur while people were in the open.

(v) *Some major catastrophic events occurring without warning, for example the accidental detonation of solid explosives, or lightning strike*
In these situations, it may not be possible to take any prior emergency action. However, most such events are of very short duration. The emergency response in these circumstances is to rescue, treat the injured, extinguish any secondary fires and mitigate any further damage.

Toxic releases

(a) The consequences of toxic releases may be more difficult to accurately predict than those of flammable releases because they are more time dependent and variable according to the distance from the release and the weather conditions. Operators should be able to estimate the concentrations and durations of gas clouds at various distances from the point of release. This information may then be used with human vulnerability models to calculate the distances at which toxic effects might be expected, and hence the area in which appropriate emergency measures might be needed. The operator should estimate dispersion distances for various foreseeable events based on the toxicology of the material involved.

(b) Different events involving the release of toxic material may require different planned responses, for example:

(i) *A slow or intermittent release, for example through a leaking relief valve*
If it was expected that the release would not be controlled quickly, or would grow with time, the appropriate response might be to evacuate the people nearest to the establishment of release and most closely downwind of it, provided that this evacuation would increase their safety. The benefits from the evacuation (shelter from the toxic release in the safe area) should outweigh any associated harm (being exposed to the toxic release during the evacuation process).

(ii) *A fire or mechanical damage that threatened an installation containing toxic material*
If the fire could not be controlled and if there was likely to be a reasonable period before overpressurisation or plant failure occurred, evacuation might be appropriate. Priority should be given to those nearest to the plant and downwind of it.

(iii) *Rapid events with a limited duration, for example the fracture of a component that could be isolated within a reasonable time*

For events that grow and can be rapidly controlled, the proposed emergency response should not include evacuation. Any toxic cloud formed would be of limited size and likely to drift past a particular spot relatively quickly. For members of the public, the best place to be located would normally be indoors, upstairs with the doors (internal and external) and windows closed, in a room which faces away from the direction of the incident.

(iv) *A major event leading to a sudden release of a large quantity of toxic substance, which would form a large toxic cloud, for example most of the contents of a storage tank escaping to the atmosphere through the failure of the tank shell*

Although the probability of such an event occurring should be extremely low, the consequences for people located close to the incident would be severe. The emergency response in these circumstances would be to rescue local people, treat the injured, make safe the affected areas and mitigate any further releases.

(c) In most cases, releases of toxic clouds tend to be hazardous down to much lower concentrations than flammable clouds, and therefore remain hazardous over greater distances when dispersing. In all cases, however, the hazard is greatest close to the source and near to the downwind plume. In many cases, the best course is not to attempt evacuation, but to go indoors and to close the doors and windows, and to switch off any ventilation and heating which draw air in from outside. In addition, if this action is followed, people will be situated where they can receive communications via radio, television or telephone. Also, if the decision is taken to evacuate, they are in a fixed location to be picked up and transported to a place of safety outside the immediate hazard zone. After the toxic cloud has passed, it is essential to get people to open all doors and windows and then to go outside until their homes are adequately ventilated.

Appendix 2: Information needs of the emergency services

The emergency services require specific information for the development of their arrangements for dealing with a major hazard accident. Operators should co-operate as much as possible with the emergency services in the collection and provision of this information, which is outlined in the following paragraphs.

Fire service

Premises and establishment-specific information on manufacturing process and hazards

(a) Provide information in non-technical terms on the establishment layout of buildings, plant and process activity, including any other associated hazards, for example electrical transformers, sub-stations and heat treatment baths.

(b) Identify the location of the emergency control centre (ECC) and any designated alternative, together with identifying key personnel, in particular specialists on site to give advice aimed at assisting with an active and dynamic risk assessment process during an emergency.

(c) Identify the location of any establishment fire service, emergency medical or first-aid centres.

(d) Confirm the inventory levels and possible ranges (maxima and minima) of notifiable hazardous substances on site and their physical states (solids, liquids, gases, fumes, vapours, micro-organisms, explosives, flammables and radioactive materials).

(e) Provide information outlining the availability of technical data from hazard sheets (Control of Substances Hazardous to Health Regulations) that gives general data on the properties and physical nature of substances likely to be encountered in storage or process plant. Identify where there is a significant risk from either a high or low pressure, high or low temperature, or catalytic reaction during a manufacturing process. Information should include how to obtain additional and more detailed data.

(f) Provide information on the details of fixed fire protection installations (for example roof ventilators, sprinklers, drenchers, fire shutters) together with technical details relevant to their operation, and the provision of any back-up installations.

(g) Indicate any loading and unloading installations together with technical details relevant to their operation, and the provision of any back-up installations.

(h) Identify, in consultation with the appropriate environment agency, the characteristics of watercourses, interceptors and plant drainage systems which aim to mitigate the environmental pollution off-site, and identification of any equipment required to assist in this, for example drain protectors, absorbents and booms.

(i) Identify any large above or below ground oil or gas pipelines serving the establishment, or supplying products for storage or process.

(j) Provide details of the type and capability of any establishment monitoring equipment for evaluating toxic, flammable or radioactive emissions, together with systems capable of giving meteorological information and of providing plume modelling.

(k) Confirm the type of security regimes employed by operators (for example electrified fences, guard dogs) which might affect operational tactics.

Means of access/egress

(a) Determine a strategy for an all hazards safe approach to the establishment, with alternatives wherever practicable.

(b) Identify access and safe routes within the establishment boundary, in particular for fire service aerial appliances and other specialised vehicles, giving consideration to available headroom, width, ground clearance, hard standing turning circles and load restrictions.

(c) Identify any construction features or structural hazards which may have a profound effect on fire fighting or rescue operations, including:

    (i) potential for rapid fire spread or production of large columns of smoke and toxic products;

    (ii) lack of compartmentation;

    (iii) unprotected shafts or openings;

    (iv) substantial basement areas; and

    (v) high potential for structural collapse.

Location of services

(a) Indicate the location and availability in an emergency of the main isolation switches and valves for product lines and essential services such as gas, electricity and water intakes.

(b) Identify the existence of automatic fire detection and suppression systems, including the type of system and their respective control points.

(c) Confirm the availability of emergency power supplies or lighting.

Water supplies

(a) Identify in collaboration with the statutory water undertaker, the availability and adequacy of water supplies for fire fighting, cooling of vessels or suppression of gas and vapour plumes, including:

    (i) type of water supply (mains, hydrants, open or static tanks);

    (ii) output available (in litres per minute) and the duration of the supply;

    (iii) availability of such systems to protect specific plant, installations and certain processes.

(b) Include estimated demand calculations for a serious fire situation, to include demands on supply from fixed installations.

(c) Consider the potential for fire water run-off being reused for fire-fighting operations.

(d) Confirm the location of manual activation or override points for fire pumps and fixed installations.

(e) Detail any alternative water supplies if there is likely to be restricted access due to radiated heat or toxic gas emissions.

(f) Confirm quantities of water available from alternative supplies and whether any seasonal changes can be expected.

Tactical fire fighting

(a) Identify suitable siting for initial attendance, including reinforcing support through designated rendezvous points and considering dependency on wind speed and direction, and giving alternatives.

(b) Develop a pre-planned strategy to make maximum use of fire-fighting jets, monitors and foam-making equipment for a major fire. Consider means of protection from surrounding exposure risks.

(c) Develop a pre-planned strategy to estimate the maximum quantities of fire water run-off, and to estimate storage lagoon and catchment areas which may be required if there is a likelihood of this water polluting watercourses.

(d) Consider the likely extent of breathing apparatus commitment, personal protective equipment and decontamination measures, including the need for safe and suitable locations, and supportive equipment and materials.

(e) Identify the best locations in which to site fire service command units, breathing apparatus control and special appliances, in order to maximise the overall control of the incident. Consideration should be given to identifying any communication dead spots.

(f) Identify the potential for an extraordinary mobilisation of bulk foam of CO_2 (concentrate type and percentage), sand dry powder, or other agents to contain the incident, and estimate the quantities required together with contacts and time of arrival on site.

(g) Confirm those substances on site with a potential to have adverse effects on fire service personal protective equipment. List any establishment specialist safety equipment (hydrofluoric acid suits) and related safety procedures, and decontamination facilities.

(h) Provide details of establishment medical assistance available, and list the nearest receiving hospital for chemical or toxic exposure, contamination and treatment, and whether antidotes are required and are available.

(i) Consider any other major factors with a potential to affect the overall control of an incident (environmental impact, airborne and/or through water) with mitigatory action required.

(j) List the salvage priorities and order for dealing with each potential loss identified.

(k) Identify the availability of mechanisms which can ensure the safe emergency shutdown of plant or equipment, and the impact of those emergency isolations on other items of plant, essential equipment or the manufacturing process.

(l) Identify the availability of on-site communications facilities and additionally any areas where there is a requirement for intrinsically safe radios (this has implications for other services).

Life risk

(a) Identify the number of people likely to be on site at any one time (day and night) and the relevant evacuation procedures, especially if people with disabilities are present.

(b) Consider the use of assembly points or refuges, and the need for the fire service to receive confirmation of roll calls.

(c) Review policies and processes designed to advise the public of the risks involved.

Police

In general terms, the police require the following information:

Site and incident-specific information

(a) Name and telephone number of the site.

(b) Number of employees on site.

(c) Description of the incident - exactly what has happened and any known hazards to assess the severity.

(d) Exact location of the site and access points - with alternatives and safe routes.

(e) Details of chemicals involved - spelling and UN numbers.

(f) The potential effects in general terms.

(g) Local wind speed and direction (if known by the site).

(h) An assessment of potential off-site implications, if known.

(i) Any proactive action the public should take.

(j) Details of casualties and/or fatalities.

(k) Actions being taken to overcome the event.

Police response

(a) *Initial action* - any special action (particular to the establishment) which needs to be taken, together with any health and safety advice for officers responding, eg is intrinsically safe equipment needed?

(b) *First response* - where and with whom the police should liaise at the scene.

On-site control details

(a) Identify the location of the ECC(s).

(b) Identify the key personnel (names and/or posts) and contact details.

Ambulance service

Establishment information required by the ambulance service

(a) Identify the location and access points - with alternatives.

(b) Confirm the commercial operation - what the establishment does.

(c) Detail the hazardous inventory - chemicals used and stored on the establishment (with quantities).

(d) Identify the main hazard - eg fire, explosion or toxic release.

(e) Provide details of the establishment medical personnel and facilities.

(f) Confirm the number of staff on site - day and night.

(g) Identify the location of the ECC(s).

(h) Identify the key personnel (names and/or posts) and contact details.

(i) Provide access to establishment plans showing the layout of the site.

(j) Provide information to allow the ambulance service to carry out a risk assessment to determine the requirement for personal protective equipment (PPE) due to chemicals used on the establishment.

(k) Detail the designated safe areas for decontamination.

(l) Identify the location of any landing zone for a helicopter air ambulance.

Health authority/board

Establishment information required by receiving hospitals

(a) Confirm the commercial operation - what the establishment does.

(b) Provide a list of chemicals used and stored on the establishment (chemical name and UN number).

(c) For each chemical detail:

  (i) chemical form;

  (ii) known risks to health;

  (iii) known treatments;

  (iv) existence and access to antidote on the site.

(d) List the contact telephone numbers.

(e) Provide information to allow the health authorities to carry out a risk assessment to determine the requirement for PPE due to chemicals used on the establishment.

Appendix 3: Organisations with roles to play in major accidents

The organisations detailed in this appendix have different roles to play in the response to emergency situations in relation to major accident hazards. A number of the sections are drawn from the Home Office publication, *Dealing with disaster* and the Scottish Office publication *Dealing with disasters together*.

Police service

The police co-ordinate all the activities of those responding at and around the scene, which must, unless a disaster has been caused by severe weather or other natural phenomena, be preserved to provide evidence for subsequent enquiries and possibly criminal proceedings. Where practicable, the police establish cordons to facilitate the work of the other emergency services in the saving of life, the protection of the public and the care of survivors. They oversee any criminal investigation. They facilitate inquiries carried out by the responsible accident investigation body, such as the Health and Safety Executive or the Air or Marine Accident Investigation Branch. The police process casualty information, and have responsibility for identifying and arranging for the removal of the dead.

Fire service

The first concerns of the fire service are to rescue people trapped in a fire, or in wreckage or debris. They prevent further escalation of the disaster by extinguishing fires or undertaking measures to prevent them. They deal with released chemicals or other contaminants in order to render the site safe. They assist the ambulance service with casualty handling and the police with recovery of bodies.

The fire service is responsible for the health and safety of personnel of all agencies working within the inner cordon, and liaise with the police about who should be allowed access to ensure that they are properly equipped, adequately trained and briefed.

Fire services' powers are derived from the Fire Services Act 1947 which, among other things, gives the senior fire service officer present at any fire the control of all operations for the extinction of that fire (section 30 (3)) and also empowers fire authorities to use their fire services for other purposes than fighting fires (section 3 (1) (e)). The fire service also works with the Agencies to safeguard the environment.

Ambulance service

The ambulance service, in conjunction with the medical incident officer and medical teams, seeks to save life and limb through effective treatment at the scene and by transporting the injured in order of priority to receiving hospitals. They will determine the hospital(s) to which injured people should be taken, which may depend on the types of injuries received. They will notify the designated hospital(s). The ambulance service response will be in line with the health service arrangements for dealing with chemical incidents under the Ambulance Service Association guidelines. Individual services may wish to implement locally agreed policies and procedures.

Coastguard

The primary responsibility of HM Coastguard is to initiate and co-ordinate civil maritime search and rescue within the United Kingdom Search and Rescue Region. This includes mobilising, organising and despatching resources to assist people in distress or in danger on the cliffs or shoreline. The Marine Pollution Unit is responsible for dealing with pollution from ships at sea and for co-ordinating the shoreline clean-up.

Local authorities

In the immediate aftermath of a disaster, the principal concerns of local authorities include: support for the emergency services; support and care for the local and wider community; use of resources to mitigate the effects of the emergency; and co-ordination of the response by organisations, other than the emergency services. As time goes on, and the emphasis switches to recovery, the local authority takes a leading role in rehabilitating the community and restoring the environment.

Adjacent local authorities and emergency services

Nearby local authorities and emergency services should provide back-up support as resources become over-stretched or if they need to implement their own emergency plans in the case of escalation.

Competent authority (HSE and EA or SEPA)

EA or SEPA will be a part of the off-site strategic co-ordinating group and the Agencies have a specific role in dealing with the environmental aspects of the emergency. The competent authority may also be involved in collecting evidence for potential prosecutions.

Health authority/board

Health authorities in England and Wales, and health boards in Scotland, are responsible for ensuring that satisfactory arrangements are in place for handling the public health and health care aspects of the response to a major accident. They contract with NHS hospital trusts, community health trusts, ambulance trusts and general practitioners to ensure an effective health response in the event of a disaster. They have overall responsibility for public health within their geographical areas, and are therefore required to have arrangements in place for the control of communicable diseases and non-communicable environmental hazards.

Utility companies

Water companies/authorities have responsibility for establishing procedures for protecting or decontaminating water supplies, maintaining sewerage treatment facilities and protecting the aquatic environment. Gas and electricity generating companies have responsibilities for restoring essential services, and telephone companies for establishing special communication arrangements.

Media

The media have their own job to do during an emergency but can perform a useful function in terms of dealing with the incident. They can provide a communication route to the public to keep them informed of progress and explain any action that they should take. For this reason they should be included in the planning process wherever possible.

Voluntary organisations

Voluntary organisations can assist in providing first aid, humanitarian assistance, environmental protection and restoration activities. They will always be under the control of a statutory authority.

Other government departments

The Ministry of Agriculture, Fisheries and Food in England, has responsibility when crops or other agricultural food sources may have been contaminated. The Scottish Office Agriculture, Environment and Fisheries Department has similar responsibilities in Scotland. The Welsh Office, Agricultural Department has responsibility for contamination incidents which may affect the food chain in Wales.

Operator

The operator activates the on-site emergency plan and communicates the incident to the relevant authorities (or has in place adequate arrangements to initiate the plan). The operator co-ordinates the on-site emergency response until the emergency services arrive, and then co-operates fully with the emergency services in dealing with the incident (see also paragraph 199).

REFERENCES AND FURTHER READING

References

1   *A guide to the Control of Major Accident Hazards Regulations 1999 (COMAH). Guidance on regulations* L111 HSE Books 1999 ISBN 0 7176 1604 5

2   *Preparing safety reports: Control of Major Accident Hazards Regulations 1999 (COMAH)* HSG190 HSE Books 1999 ISBN 0 7176 1687 8

3   *The Planning (Control of Major-Accident Hazards) Regulations 1999* SI 1999/981 The Stationery Office 1999 ISBN 0 11 082367 2

4   Home Office *Dealing with disaster* (Third edition) Brodie Publishing 1997 ISBN 185 893 9208

5   Scottish Office *Dealing with disasters together* (Second edition) 1998, available from The Scottish Office Emergency Planning Branch: Tel 0131 244 2184

6   *Planning for major incidents: the NHS guidance* 1998, available on the Department of Health website www.open.gov.uk/doh/epcu/epcu/index.htm

7   *A manual of guidance responding to emergencies - guidance for the NHS in Scotland* 1998, available on the Scottish Office Department of Health website www.show.scot.nhs.uk/dtc

8   Environment Agency *Guidance on the interpretation of major accidents to the environment for the purposes of the COMAH Regulations* The Stationery Office 1999

9   *Chemicals (Hazard Information and Packaging for Supply) Regulations 1994* SI 1994/3247 The Stationery Office 1994 ISBN 0 11 043877 9 (as amended 1996, 1997, 1998 and 1999)

10   *The exercise planners guide* Home Office 1999, available on the Home Office website www.homeoffice.gov.uk/epd

Further reading

Be prepared for an emergency: Guidance for emergency planning Chemical Industries Association 1991 ISBN 0 900623 54 3

Emergency procedures manual Association of Chief Police Officers 1997 update available on disk. Apply to ACC (Operations) Cleveland Constabulary

Fire service major incident emergency procedures manual 1994

Ambulance service operational arrangements for civil emergencies Ambulance Service Association, available from ASA National Office, Tel: 020 7921 5100

Model off-site emergency plan Contingency Planning Group, Operations Department, London Fire & Civil Defence Authority 1997, available on The Society of Industrial Emergency Services Officers (SIESO) website www.sieso.ndirect.co.uk

Murray Virginia (editor) *Major chemical disasters - medical aspects of management* Royal Society of Medicine 1990 ISBN 1 85315 104 1

Be prepared for an emergency: Training and exercises Chemical Industries Association 1992 ISBN 0 900623 73 X

Printed and published by the Health and Safety Executive   C17.5 1/03